Landforms of Australia

Water cuts into fragmenting sandstone cliffs at Fitzroy Falls

Limestone forms in Lake Cave, Margaret River; and (opposite) the sea-eroded limestone cliffs of Anxious Bay, Great Australian Bight

Vincent Serventy

LANDFORMS
OF AUSTRALIA

AMERICAN ELSEVIER PUBLISHING COMPANY, INC.

NEW YORK 1968

Contents

Vincent Serventy

Vincent Serventy, author of various books on natural history, was at one time Senior Lecturer in charge of Science and Mathematics at Claremont Teachers' College; he gained his degrees of Bachelor of Science and Bachelor of Education from the University of Western Australia. In acknowledging his debt to the University faculty he says: ". . . I was fortunate in having teachers such as the late Professor E. de C. L. Clarke and Professor Rex Prider. Professor R. Fairbridge and Professor J. Wells helped me with particular problems, and Dr A. R. Main was of great assistance in reviewing my ideas for this book."

Library of Congress Catalog Card No.: 68-17759

American Edition Published in 1968 *by*
AMERICAN ELSEVIER PUBLISHING COMPANY, INC.
52 Vanderbilt Avenue
New York, New York 10017

PRINTED IN AUSTRALIA

Deep valley of limestone cut by Bungonia Creek, near Goulburn, New South Wales

I
Nature as a sculptor

IF the passage of time could be compressed so that a million years flowed past each second, and if we could watch the spectacle from a spaceship high above the Earth, this land of Australia would present a marvellous variety of changing forms.

We would see it, at one moment, a mountainous and rugged continent—but not in the outline we know today. Then the forces of erosion would wear away the mountains, washing the spoil into the sea. Huge sections of the continent would disappear under the ocean, then reappear bringing back the spoil as hardened sediments—sandstone, shale, and so on. Volcanoes would pour out lava flows, great ice sheets would cover parts of the continent, then these would melt and deserts spread.

As the landforms changed, the march of evolution would bring new plants and new animals. For a time giant dinosaurs would tramp the land, then they too would go.

In the last few minutes, from this bewildering kaleidoscope of shifting mountains, deserts, plains and rivers, would emerge the Australia of today.

To understand the Australian landscape we need to know how the land was first made, how it changed through millions of years, and finally, how, under the moulding hand of our present climate and plants and animals, it took the form we know today.

We will look in later chapters at the Australian pattern in more detail, but here are a few basic facts: Our land has often been described as the earth's largest island or smallest continent. Its three million square miles are bounded by eleven thousand miles of ocean on the mainland and nine thousand miles in Tasmania. Yet a continent should not only be considered in terms of what is above the surface but also in terms of the shelf and the shallow seas surrounding it. This continental shelf is measured to the point where the sea is only six hundred feet deep. Beyond that point the shelf becomes a steep slope falling away into the ocean abyss. If we look at a map that shows this shelf, then Australia increases only slightly on the east and west coasts, but Tasmania and New Guinea become linked with the mainland.

How it all began

It is now generally believed that the continents have been constant features of the earth scene, floating like lighter icebergs on a denser ground mass of rock. Whether the continents always stayed put or whether they drifted like real icebergs is a hotly debated question. The theory of continental drift helps explain many problems, both of shapes of continents and of similarities between their rocks and the plants and animals that live on these land masses.

Imagine the primeval continent rising above the primeval sea. Nature would slowly wear away the land until it became reduced to a low-lying plain, a peneplain. Once the slope became gentle enough the natural forces wearing away the rock would almost cease. Many coastal plains in Australia have reached this stage. Then the land would be thrust high above the sea once more. Other parts of the continent would sink below it. These movements are called tectonic, and are the ones most people have read about and understand. With such movements go a shaking of the earth—an earthquake. Sometimes man can see this happen-

5

ing dramatically. The sea may flood the land, or it may retreat, leaving the sea bottom as dry land.

There is also a more subtle way in which this can take place. In a railway carriage when two trains pass each other, it is not always easy for passengers to know which train is moving. When land emerges from the sea or submerges below it, we cannot always be sure if it is due to the land rising or sinking, or the sea rising or sinking. When it is the sea that moves, scientists call it a eustatic movement.

How can the sea level change?

One way is when the shape of the ocean basins alters, becoming either deeper or shallower. Apparently this does happen, but how and why is not yet understood.

It would seem at first thought that the volume of the sea must remain roughly the same. Perhaps a little water trapped deep in rocks could be released to flow back into the sea, but this would make little difference. However there are two ways in which sea levels can change. When materials are heated, they become larger. When cooled, they contract. It has been worked out that a drop in temperature of one degree centigrade in the waters of the oceans would mean a drop of six feet in ocean level as the water shrank with cooling. Again it has been worked out that the temperature of the oceans during the last million years may have varied as much as five degrees centigrade. This could mean a change in level of thirty feet.

These are still only minor changes, but there is a much larger one possible. If all the ice and snow on earth today melted, it is thought by many geologists, sea levels the world over would rise between two and three hundred feet. A glance at the map of Australia would show how disastrous this could be to the settled regions of this land. If the icefields increased in size, locking up waters from the ocean as solid ice on dry land, then the oceans would shrink. In comparatively recent times the sea level stood three hundred feet lower than it does today, during the period of one of the great ice ages.

A dropping away of the sea from a continent worn down to a gentle slope could begin a new and vigorous attack on the land, as rivers took on new life and began cutting back from the sea edge.

Despite all this Australia remains today a placid land. No great mountain chains block easy passage across the continent. Much of Australia is made of ancient rocks, which indicate that our land has been a point of stability in an unstable world for a considerable period of time.

In broad terms the land falls into three sections —the western third is a plateau, an ancient shield of rocks; the Eastern Highlands are separated from this by the Central Basin. In these three major physiographic regions are a number of minor patterns of landforms.

Before we turn to study these great sections in more detail we will look at the tools nature has to shape these forms.

THE DINOSAUR FOOTPRINTS: *One hundred and twenty million years ago a dinosaur walked along an estuary edge near the town of Broome, Western Australia. A flood brought down sand to cover the prints, otherwise they would have been washed away with the next tide. With the passing of years more sand was added. Over millions of years the sand changed to sandstone, first below the sea, then finally raised above it. Today the sandstone forms a line of cliffs and continues as reefs under the sea. The sea wore away at the rock until the old prints were once more brought to the light of day*

6

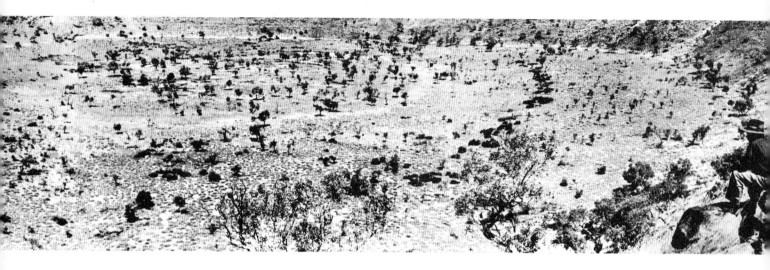

WOLF CREEK METEORITE CRATER: *One of the world's largest meteorite craters occurs in the northwest of Australia. This was discovered in 1947, officially at least, though it was known to travellers in this area long before. It is about 5 square miles in area and about 2800 feet across. The central section is within a hundred feet of the surface level and supports trees. The rim rock is a hundred feet above the surrounding plain, so the crater lip rises two hundred feet above the base. About a ton of oxidized fragments have been recovered from the surroundings and some of these have unaltered metal as a core. The southwest rim is high and this is an indication of a meteorite coming fairly slowly from the northwest. It is believed to have fallen in the last million years, but how big it was has not yet been worked out. This remarkable crater is said to be the one on earth that shows the closest resemblance to those found on the moon. An attempt is being made to get this crater declared a National Park.*

Craters formed by meteorites are unusual and those in Australia have created great interest. Central Australia has two well-known ones. That at Henbury consists of a number of small craters, with the largest 660 feet in diameter and 60 feet deep. These are south of Alice Springs. About 170 miles to the north-east is the Boxhole Crater which is slightly smaller than the largest one found at Henbury. Not all meteorites striking the ground form craters. It seems as though a combination of a large meteorite and the heat of impact results in an explosion which makes the crater

2
The work of sun and air

CONSTANT DRIPPING wears away the hardest stone. In this fragment of folk-lore is the key to the story of how nature carves the land into the shapes we know. Ancient philosophers, seeing the hollow gradually ground into a stone under a dripping fountain, seized on this as a precept for man to keep on trying. Builders of paths, of steps, of floors, noticed how, through the years, the solid material was literally rubbed away by the steady pounding of innumerable feet. Along the seashores man watched as huge waves lifted giant rocks from the sea bed and hurled them like battering rams at cliff faces to bring the solid rock tumbling into ruin. With terror he saw stout ships picked up and smashed to pieces on off-shore reefs. Great flooding rivers or rising seas destroyed cities, and such cataclysms became enshrined in his legends.

Yet with all these examples of the sculptural hands of nature before his eyes he could not take the mental step to realize that the mountains and the huge valleys in which he lived had also been carved by those same forces. For ancient man, a valley was the product of some giant cataclysm when the earth was split asunder. But even in those far off times there were some men who could guess the story behind the landforms they saw about them. Two thousand years ago Herodotus estimated that if the Nile ran into the Red Sea it would fill it entirely with silt in ten thousand years.

Most men accepted the belief that the land they saw about them had at one time been created and would continue as it was. The Australian Aborigines had a mythological explanation for everything in their tribal territory. Ayers Rock, for example, in the legends of the Pitjandjara people was made in the Dreamtime. The southern face was created during a battle between the poisonous snakes and the carpet snakes. The hare wallabies made the northern face of the rock. Three hundred miles to the north the men of Yuendumu showed me their sacred snake painting and told me how the huge snake came out of the south. As it writhed along it created the valleys. Then it rested at this spot before travelling north. The cave in the cliff was where it had lain. So man, ever seeking explanation, needed legends to explain his world.

During the scientific revolution of the last two hundred years man began to look more searchingly at the earth about him. Like a detective who examines the scene of a crime and then works back till he discovers each step that led to the final result, the geologists, looking at the landforms about them and studying what was happening to these forms by land, sea, and air were able to trace back through the stages when the land was first heaved up above the oceans. Piece by piece the jigsaw is fitted together. From the past the scientist is able to predict the future development of the landforms, and in minor ways to try to stay their course where it suits present needs.

Why then did it take so long for man to realize that the key to the landforms about him lay in the simple things at work on the land—the tools of water, sun, and air? The explanation is simple.

The dripping water took a hundred years to wear away a foot of rock. A hundred thousand years would be needed to wear away a thousand feet of rock. To explain all the landforms on this earth we must push back our time scale, not only

STONE KANGAROO: *This rock is probably a glacial erratic put up in the Great Victoria Desert, Western Australia, by the natives of the area. For them it represented the sacred kangaroo and played an important part in ceremonies*

into thousands, but into thousands of millions of years.

The tools nature uses can be seen at work all about us. Inside our house, on the walls, on the roof, in the yard, in the street, on the beach. In some parts of Australia we can see the tools working in a spectacular way. In others we must use creative imagination to find the clues. Science has a word for this study. *Geo* means earth and *morph* means shape. Put them together and we have geomorphology, the science of landforms.

It is exciting that the last fifteen years have seen a minor revolution in this study. Classic explanations of how the land was shaped have been found wanting and there is now a new ferment in this field. So it is best to hold all *present explanations* as tentative.

The weapons nature uses to reduce rock to soil and mountains to plains are many and varied. The earliest to begin work on the earth was the sun. The astronaut who is first to land on the moon will be able to judge how effective the sun is, for on the moon there seems to be no wind, no air, no rain, no plants and no animals. Only the changing temperatures can have any effect. It is believed that a layer of dust covers the moon's surface, particles broken off by the heat from the sun that expands the rock; then with the cool of night contraction causes the upper layers to split away. We see exactly the same kind of fracturing when a thick glass is plunged into boiling water. In a multicoloured rock the dark minerals heat up more than the light ones, and so the rock begins to crumble. Anyone who has slept in a house with an iron roof knows well the steady crackling of the iron as it expands by day and shrinks by night. In deserts where a rock surface may rise to a temperature of a hundred and fifty degrees by day

WOMAN AND KANGAROO: *The breakaway country in Arnhem Land is renowned for its magnificent Aboriginal art galleries. Here is a pictorial story of one of the ancient myths about the creation of this country in the Dreamtime*

10

SACRED SNAKE: *This immense painting of the sacred snake, at Yuendumu, is a tribute to its mythological significance in creating much of the country near this spot about two hundred miles northwest of Alice Springs*

PEGMATITE VEIN IN GNEISS: *The difference in colours of rocks helps in breaking them up. The light coloured vein is a pegmatite which has been forced into the ground rock of gneiss (Western Australia)*

11

DOLERITE BOULDERS: *These boulders of fine grained dolerite, in Tasmania, have weathered into a soft clay in a characteristic spheroidal fashion*

and drop below freezing by night, the moment when a rock finally shatters may produce frightening noises. A hundred-foot-long boulder of granite may expand an inch during the period from the chill of midnight to the heat of midday. It is only the surface layer that moves, since rock is a poor conductor of heat. This layer splits off, and we call this exfoliation.

In addition, when water penetrates such cracks, cold air may freeze it. Anyone who has driven in the Australian Alps in winter knows what happens to the radiator of a car that contains pure water with no antifreeze in it. The same expansion that shatters the radiator, shatters the rocks.

On mountain slopes small angular fragments lie on the lower slopes, broken away by either heat or frost from the bare rock above. Such talus or scree slopes are common throughout Australia. This kind of rock breakdown we call mechanical weathering.

Varying heat from molten rocks forced to the surface, and the earthquake shocks produced by the earth's crust settling out of strain into a more stable position, can cause more fracturing. At the Devil's Marbles in Central Australia, magnificent examples can be seen of boulders ten feet in diameter and twenty feet long cleft into two parts by a combination of many such forces. Yet the

12

effects of expansion and contraction only start the work and are minor tools.

All around us are the combined effects of warmth and damp air. An old can on the side of the road in a few years rusts away. A deserted house, after a hundred years, shows only low crumbling walls. A thousand years and only an archaeologist would know that a house once existed. Thriving cities of two or three thousand years ago have disappeared entirely, leaving only traces below the soil.

Chemical changes are one of the most potent weapons nature has to convert solid rock into fragments. The oxygen and carbon dioxide in the air in the presence of water can produce extraordinary results. Such chemical weathering for example, can change the black iron ore known as magnetite into the red or yellow iron ore known as limonite. In the act of changing from magnetite to limonite the crystals swell and help fracture the rock.

One of the best-known and most common examples is the breakdown of solid granite into soil. Three important minerals in granite are white felspar, glassy silica and black mica. Felspar combines with water and carbon dioxide to change into a clay called kaolin, and releases silica and other salts. Silica is one of the stable minerals

DEVIL'S MARBLES: *These granite residuals are a famous landform found about sixty miles south of Tennant Creek in the Northern Territory. Granite often weathers into rounded shapes as exfoliation peels off layer after layer till nothing remains. Some of the boulders however have broken across lines of weakness called joints*

CLUB LAKE, AUSTRALIAN ALPS: *Here is a glacial lake dammed by a moraine and now filling the cirque produced during the last ice period when these mountains had their own glaciers*

A VOLCANIC DYKE: *Here a fine-grained dark igneous rock called epidiorite runs as a huge vein through granite. Where the molten rock was forced through the granite, the quicker cooling near the edge can be seen on the left hand of the picture. On the surface the epidiorite weathers to a rich red soil, much favoured by farmers, while the granite weathers to a poorer sandy soil. Even when the soil is covered with plants, the below-soil rock can be worked out by the kind of plants that grow there. On the soil above granite, eucalypt trees known as Marri and Jarrah are common. On the red clays of the epidiorite grow white barked Wandoos*

14

DURICRUST: *When a cutting is made in the soil, the pattern of weathering shows well. Here at the top is a thin section of soil, then the hard red duricrust, then white clay and finally untouched granite, the mother rock*

MUD CRACKS: *The pattern shown by drying mud may be preserved as a fossil structure. Also just as drying mud breaks up in this way, so molten rock develops lines of weakness or joints, which show up in the rock when it outcrops on the surface*

that are very important in the surface layers of the earth. What most people call sand is grains of silica.

So we can see that, even on a perfectly flat surface of bare rock, mechanical and chemical weathering can produce a soil that entirely covers the parent rock. Digging will often reveal four layers, first the surface soil often blackish in colour, a paler subsoil with bits of rock scattered through it, then crumbling rock, and finally bedrock.

A most interesting rock formation that is an outstanding feature of landforms is variously called ironstone, gravel, laterite, and duricrust. This thick armour of rock, which often caps hills in the Australian area, is also found at times buried beneath a layer of soil, and then may be called hardpan. The hard layer may have a thickness of a foot or may reach depths of fifty feet. It passes into a less cemented layer, then into weathered rock and finally into unweathered rock. It

Colour

STONE ARRANGEMENT AT BOO-YOO-NOO: *These lumps of ironstone have been set into a pattern (Top). Along these paths young men travelled in their initiation ceremonies. This was an important ceremonial site for the natives of the Great Victoria Desert (Western Australia)*

MOUNT DAVIS, CANNING STOCK ROUTE: *This range is made of sandstone and shows the structure known as current bedding (Lower). In shallow water, where currents are both swift and changeable, sand may be deposited, not on long flat beds but in tumbled heaps. When these harden they give all the appearance of having been distorted by earth movements (Western Australia)*

BRACHINA GORGE: *A huge lump of rock weighing possibly a hundred tons slides downhill in this gorge in the Flinders Ranges*

16

GIBBER PLAINS: *Irregular rock fragments strewn over the floor of this stony desert in South Australia*

RED SAND DUNE: *Throughout the inland country moving red dunes (Top) are a feature usually where over-grazing has removed the plant cover (Northern Territory)*

FIXED DUNE, GREAT VICTORIA DESERT: *A typical scene in the sandridge country (Lower). This area has never been grazed and the dunes are fixed. These dunes occur about every quarter of a mile and run for hundreds of miles in an east-west direction (Western Australia)*

does not really matter what the bedrock is—granite, gneiss, schist—all produce a duricrust. The chemicals in this layer may vary, and in parts of Australia that are rich in bauxite this is mined as an aluminium ore. Other parts of Australia are rich in iron oxides, and in some places there is mostly silica. Although duricrust may consist of many fragments of rock coated with the various oxides, some of the rounder pebbles often show layer after layer of material, just like a pearl. In other words the round "gravel" is built up over a period of years with layer after layer of chemicals deposited on a nucleus, perhaps a fragment of the original rock before weathering.

How does it form? There are several theories and perhaps each or some combination of these may have played a part, depending on circumstances.

In dry climates the occasional rains that fall will soak through the soil, dissolving away various

DESERT GLAZE: *The pebbles in this desert scene in Western Australia shine like glass. Each is coated with layers of iron and manganese oxides*

minerals that lie there. The water travels on to the water table, the section of the soil that is completely water saturated. With dry periods this water would be drawn up once more by capillarity, leaving behind the minerals. A similar action, still going on today, forms the famous "desert glaze" of our inland deserts where a level surface covered with pebbles will glisten like glass.

Another theory is that the duricrust formed when the climate resembled "wet tropic". Under humid conditions minerals are quickly decomposed and carried into the subsoil, where they deposit to form a hardpan. With the coming of the great dry, the impoverished sand above the hardpan, deprived of its plant cover, would quickly be blown away, leaving the hardpan as a surface crust.

It is impossible to separate entirely the effects of this weathering from the work of plants and animals, many of which are microscopic. It is interesting to look at a slab of rock that still remains bare though surrounded by forest or scrub. The so-called bare rock will be found to be rough and pitted. A close look will show that it is covered with a black material. This will be one of the lowly groups of plants known as alga. These plants help to decompose the rock surface. Also there will be patches of that strange plant partnership called a lichen, when fungus and alga work together to colonize a most inhospitable environment. As these plants help make a thin film of soil, the mosses move in. Hard on the heels of the mosses come small shrubs. When these pioneers have developed enough thickness of soil by their roots splitting the rock and by chemical exudates, still more shrubs and trees invade, finally rolling like a great green wave over the once bare rock. This kind of climax faces every bare rock surface, once it comes above the sea.

RECHERCHE ARCHIPELAGO: *Here the bare rock shows the steady attack of the elements. In the foreground algae and lichens attack the bare rock. Pigface and other plants help build up the soil, and layers of rock break away from the bed rock. Under the layers shelter small animals like these barking lizards. The white animal is casting its skin*

NOONFLOWER ON GRANITE: *Here a succulent plant creeps over bare rock. The solutions from its roots and decaying leaves will help disintegrate the rock surface (Tasmania)*

BOYAGIN ROCK: *A huge granite dome heaves above a forest in Western Australia. With the passage of time the forest will cover the bare rock whose slopes are too steep to hold erosion products*

DOG ROCK: *This strange formation in Albany, Western Australia, is a residual of the erosion of the local rock, and stands in the main street of the town. The rock is gneiss, a metamorphic rock common in the southwest*

A GRANITE SURFACE: *On the bare rock are algae and lichens. Then come the mosses; then behind the mosses the needle plant. When enough soil has formed, small shrubs can grow. Finally trees appear*

GRANITE BOULDER: *This weathered lump of granite shows the typical exfoliation produced by mechanical and chemical weathering (Western Australia)*

LIMESTONE CONCRETION: *Layers of lime are laid down round a nucleus, to produce large spheres of lime. Basically the formation is similar to that of a pearl but lacks the pearl's beauty*

3
The work of wind and rain

ANYONE who has walked along a sandy beach or along the top of a sand dune in a high wind will know how painfully the sand cuts against bare legs. In world deserts where the sand is on the move, telegraph poles are sawn through in a few years and hard rocks are also worn away, more gradually. This process is called corrasion. Though not important in Australia today, it was important during the recent dry period of a few thousand years ago. It is possible that the so-called wave formations found in Wave Rock at Hyden and in many other rock outcrops on the Western Shield and also at Ayers Rock may be due to wind-driven sand. As the wind stripped the soil away from the rocks, the sand grains would cut away at deeper and deeper layers. However, since sand grains rarely rise to heights of more than two feet, this corrading effect would be restricted to a narrow zone.

Another important effect of wind is to polish grains of sand till they become almost round. Running water works very slowly on small sand grains, and it has been estimated that wind would round them off at hundreds of times the speed.

Duststorms are produced when moving sand grains bombard finer particles and lift them from the ground so that they move along on the wind. Huge storms occur at times, and residents on the east coast of Australia often experience red rain when the dust from the inland is brought to ground once more by falling water. It was estimated that one duststorm in Melbourne in 1920 brought down 64 tons of material on every square mile. Another duststorm is said to have moved 200,000 tons of soil from Australia to New Zealand, this dust having travelled 2000 miles from Central Australia. In this case Australia's loss was New Zealand's gain, though much of the topsoil removed in this way falls into the sea.

Another spectacular effect on Australian landforms is shown in sand dunes. Along the coast where iron minerals are leached away, the sand is normally white, while inland in arid places the dunes are red. At Sharks Bay red and white sand dunes can be seen lying against each other, and the greater amount of lime in the white dunes supports a very distinctive and different vegetation from that on the red dunes.

It is now thought that desert sand is made from previous sandstone rocks. Most sand in dunes is standard in size, ranging between an eighth and a quarter of a millimetre in diameter, and if a desert is made of the wrong size of particles, it never becomes a sandy desert. The gibber deserts of Central Australia, for example, contain larger pebbles coated with oxides of iron and manganese. These are highly polished and resist sand blasting.

As for the sand, at times it forms into dunes of characteristic shape. Exactly how these dunes are built is a matter of controversy. At first sight sand dunes appear to show a bewildering variety, but they are usually variations on two themes.

One basic type is shaped like a crescent and is called a barchan dune. This is thought to be created when small supplies of sand are available and with moderate winds. The horns of the crescent point in the direction the wind is blowing. Should the wind change direction often, then the crescents may multiply or the whole barchan reverse. And there are longitudinal dunes or seif dunes. Sometimes these lie across the wind direction when blown by moderate winds. If the winds be-

DRIFTING SAND DUNES: *At Greenough, south of Geraldton, sand dunes are rolling in from the sea and slowly covering farmland*

SAND DUNE IN GREAT VICTORIA DESERT: *These parallel ridges run for hundreds of miles in the desert. Usually they lie about a quarter of a mile apart and the bigger trees grow on the ridges. In the flats between can be seen Mulga and Desert Spinifex*

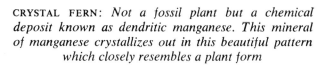

CRYSTAL FERN: *Not a fossil plant but a chemical deposit known as dendritic manganese. This mineral of manganese crystallizes out in this beautiful pattern which closely resembles a plant form*

ARTESIAN BORE: *A hole made to the water-bearing layer of an artesian basin brings the water shooting to the surface under its own pressure*

THE SHATTER BELT: *Fronting the walls of Wilpena Pound, in the Flinders Range, South Australia, are moving red sand dunes. The South Australian Highlands impress any traveller to the State. In the north are the blue peaks of the Flinders, while towering over the city of Adelaide is Mount Lofty. These original plains were lifted to form plateaus and by down warping and faulting, a series of ranges formed. Mount Lofty descends to the plains to the west in a series of steps*

EUCLA: *Drifting dunes have overwhelmed this town in Western Australia. Probably over-grazing by goats and camels started the sand moving. Today rabbits and sheep prevent the vegetation stabilizing the coastal dunes. There is also a possibility that the dry areas of Australia are becoming more arid*

27

PETRIFIED FOREST: *Although called a petrified forest, these are not really fossil fragments of wood. Actually the lime has deposited along plant roots and increased in amount after the plant died. Strong winds have now stripped away the sand cover (Western Australia)*

THE PINNACLES: *These limestone spears and pillars which formed in the sand dunes of this coastal plain north of Perth were revealed when wind stripped away the sand*

come stronger, they lie along the wind direction.

Across Central Australia are huge sandridge deserts, and these will be described later.

Rain

Australia is the driest of continents today, though this was not true a few thousand years ago. The effect of aridity has been imposed fairly recently on our landscape. Today the average rainfall is only 17 inches compared with 26 inches for the earth as a whole. One third of the continent has rain less than 10 inches, and two thirds less than 20 inches a year. So we have a picture of a continent, moist round the fringes and steadily drying out as we move away from the coast to the centre. It is this central desert that has affected the history of the country, its exploration and its mythology. Just as the sea was to Great Britain, a mystery to be explored, so the desert is always in the minds of Australians, the never never, the back of beyond, the dead heart.

Raindrops produce small landforms of interest while helping to shape the larger forms. Anyone who has walked across bare soil in a rainstorm will find his shoes spattered with soil. The raindrops, beating like tiny hammers, shoot the soil in all directions. On a slope this means that the soil gradually moves downhill. I remember my early days on a hillside farm where my father used to complain about the rocks that rose to the surface and had to be removed by hand. It was not the rocks that were rising. It was the soil that was sinking. Sometimes heavy rain will form into a sheet flood carrying soil for short distances. This can often be seen in desert places, or where bad farming has left no plant cover on the hillslopes.

After the rain has fallen, a little goes back into the air as vapour, some runs away to make creeks and rivers, and some sinks into the soil, dissolving away salts and carrying them below the surface to the water table.

RAPIDS: *A small, hard ridge creates a series of rapids in this South Australian stream. Rapids are found in young river valleys*

AERIAL SCENE IN THE AUSTRALIAN ALPS: *A typical rugged young landscape with many streams eroding narrow valleys*

30

4
The work of rivers and ice

IT was a long time before man would accept the work of rivers in providing most of the world's landforms. James Hutton in a book published in 1797 did for this branch of geology what Charles Darwin did later for biology. Both rolled away clouds of ignorance and allowed science to march forward at ever increasing speed in its understanding of the earth.

How running water wears away the soil can be seen on a small scale by turning a garden hose of water on to a hill of sand. In a few minutes you can create for yourself a tiny continent, complete with its own landforms. First you will have steep sided valleys with swift running streams. Then the valleys will broaden until finally your heap of earth has settled down to a broad plain with a river flowing, often quite swiftly between low hills. Should you lack a heap of soil in the garden, then roadsides, railway cuttings and even coastlines with a tidal range will give river patterns.

The water works in two ways. First it abrades the sides and bottom of the stream, cutting away at banks, creating waterfalls and later removing them, working like a saw that cuts both vertically and horizontally. However, every time you use a hammer to break up a rock, as Newton showed so clearly you also break up your hammer. A hammer, being tough, tends to last longer, but a rock carried along by a river gets as good as it gives. This wearing away of nature's sculpting tools is called abrasion and is similar to what happens to sand driven by the wind.

A fast-running stream is a fascinating study, and waterfalls, rapids, potholes, sandbanks, undercut river banks—all clearly show water at work.

In the stream bed the rounded boulders and coarse sand show the tools that nature uses.

As creeks and rivers tear away the hills, in other places they are busy filling in old valleys, lakes and off-shore areas. Experiments have shown that while a stream travelling at one fifth of a mile an hour moves fine clay, a stream running at two miles an hour can roll along pebbles an inch in diameter. It is thought at present that the work done by rivers the world over is similar in many respects, though future research may show major differences. An often quoted stream is the Mississippi. This is a huge river; and in Australia, because of its drier climate, the erosion indicated would not take place. In solution this river carries to the sea 136,000,000 tons of material a year. Suspended in the flowing water are 340,000,000 tons and rolling along the bottom go another 40,000,000 tons. The total effect on the land mass is to lower the river basin by one foot every four thousand years. This is a very impressive figure and shows how in certain climates the land can be quickly worn away and poured into the sea or on to lower floodplains.

However, in both their upper reaches and lower ones rivers build up as well as break down. Small sandbanks develop on the inner curve of a river bank where the water flow is sluggish. There is a corresponding undercut on the other side where the water flow is fast. Such banks do not last very long as the river continues to cut sideways. Nearer the mouth in flood years a river may spread a lot of silt on its floodplain. With the passing of years the floodplains may build up until they are beyond the reach of floodwaters. These alluvial flats are eagerly sought for farmlands.

POTHOLE: *Small pebbles swirl about, gradually enlarging the hole, till finally the bed is cut to a lower level (Western Australia)*

NATURE'S TOOLS: *Snowy River stream bed showing the rounded boulders which in flood time act as hammers to pound away the stream bed and sides*

Deltas can form at any river mouth provided the river is depositing more material than the waves, winds and tide can move away. With the rising of the sea levels over the last twenty thousand years many deltas are now hidden under the sea and large ones look smaller. The Mississippi is pushing its delta into the sea at the rate of a mile every sixteen years, showing how nature reclaims part of the sea for land.

Looking again at river channels an interesting feature can be noted even in the small channels running on steep slopes. Although they appear to be straight, a closer examination will show small meanders developing along their length. In one experiment, using a stream trough loaded with granulated perspex, two stages developed. First, alternate hollows and shallows developed; then these changed to meanders where the stream swung from side to side. But why it did is still a mystery. However, once a stream starts swinging it is easy to see how the meanders will deepen as the fast-flowing outer edge cuts into the bank and the slow-flowing inner edge begins to shoal.

Another type of river course is the braided stream. Here a wide and shallow channel carries a stream that wanders through many sandbanks.

EROSION: *A cleared paddock gives an excellent demonstration of water erosion on a small scale. This same pattern can be seen on a large scale all over Australia*

33

BENDEMEER: *This river winds through a mature New South Wales landscape. Willows are planted along the edges to hold the soil firm when the river comes down in flood*

Not a great deal is known about the causes of braided streams, though they are common in many parts of Australia.

If we look at the story of a river from birth to old age the following stages can be seen: *A very young stream* cuts a channel in the flat surface (this kind of stream is often seen in paddocks when poor farming leads to erosion). Then the very young stream merges with a young river where a deep gorge winds through hilly country. *A mature stream* has reduced very hilly country to only moderately hilly; the narrow V of the young river has widened to a broader V, the waterfalls and rapids have gone and some alluvial flats have developed. *An old river* has stopped eroding and winds leisurely through gentle slopes. Often all stages of maturity can be seen in the one river at different parts of its course.

Colour
PLATEAU, MESA AND BUTTE: *The gradual erosion of a plateau (Top) is well shown here at Pyramid Hill in the northwest of Western Australia*

YAMPIRE GORGE: *In the red quartzites of this cliff in the Hamersleys (Lower) can be seen a blue line formed of blue asbestos. An abandoned mine shaft leads into the hill*

Overleaf
NATURAL BRIDGE: *Near Albany are enormous landforms created by wave action (Top). This natural bridge is one of the stages reached in the wearing away of the rock (Western Australia)*

PLUNGING CLIFFS NEAR ALBANY: *These smooth rocks have proved a trap for many fishermen (Lower), swept to their deaths by "king" waves. The plunging cliffs allow no foothold for a swimmer to escape from the sea*

34

Geologists call this the cycle of erosion, when a land mass is lifted above the sea or an old land mass is raised or tilted. The names given to the landscapes and rivers of youth, maturity and old age are not quite apt as a human analogy. For a landscape, youth is the time of the wrinkled surface. With age comes the smoothing of contours.

It is obvious enough if we study the eastern highlands, the Darling Scarp or coastal areas of Tasmania that here are young landscapes and young rivers. Narrow V shaped valleys are full of waterfalls, rapids and potholes formed by swirling pebbles stirred by fast streams. In each landform lies the seed of its own destruction. The waterfall wears back into the obstruction that caused it and finally this is removed. Gradually the hills wear away until the river flows sluggishly through a fairly level plain with a gradual fall to the sea. The landscape has reached old age and the river senility. However, many scientific workers today feel these terms should be abandoned. Much of the earlier work was done in Europe and North America, where landscapes have felt the full im-

KANYAKA RUINS: *Here in an old valley in South Australia too much clearing and over-grazing has started erosion once more, as the streams cut into the old floodplains*

pact of huge icesheets. In Africa and Australia a different kind of landscape is common. The interior of Australia is full of flat-topped hills often called tent hills or mesas, with broad flat valleys between them. Perhaps instead of the hillslopes gradually wearing down as is usually imagined, it is rather a case of wearing back, with the hills remaining the same height but becoming smaller in bulk. The plateau breaks up into mesas and these sharpen into narrow pointed pyramid hills or buttes. It is to be stressed that we must consider landscapes not as wearing inexorably to flat plains but as continually being given injections of new energy through movements of the earth's crust and by climatic changes.

Australian Rivers

The rivers of wetter continents flow in what we think of as a normal way, from the mountains to the sea. In Australia the usual is often the opposite to what is normal elsewhere. Only round the edges of the continent does this running to the sea happen. Over half the country, the scanty rainfall flows in halfhearted fashion to fill deep

GEIKIE GORGE: *This huge meander shows how the river builds up on one side and cuts away on the other (Western Australia)*

pools along the meandering river beds. In heavy rainfall years the rivers spill out, often over hundreds of miles of plain country and finally reach journey's end, a salt lake. Such lakes, the most famous of which is Lake Eyre, though it is only the largest of many thousands, are dry most of the time. However, there are years when salt lakes in settled areas hold water long enough to become important sporting areas for boating, swimming, and water skiing. In less frequented spots they are breeding places for water birds. When normal times return the lakes dry out and their beds become a white sea of salt, glistening in the hot sun and mocking the traveller in search of water. Upstream from the lake the river dwindles to a series of pools, some of which are permanent and have passed into the Australian language under the musical name of billabong. So the droughts of inland Australia are normal, the good rains the abnormal.

The scantiness of the rainfall is well shown in the river systems. Streams that flow the whole year round, the perennials, are missing from a huge stretch of country on the west and south coasts.

COOPER CREEK: *One of the famous rivers of Central Australia in flood time spilling over its banks and creating huge, though temporary lakes*

40   RUSSELL FALLS: *This beautiful doublet of falls is in the Mount Field National Park, Tasmania. The total drop is about 150 feet*

WATERFALL, BLUE MOUNTAINS: *Most of the larger waterfalls are found in the Eastern Highlands. The highest in Australia is at Wollomombi in northeastern New South Wales. Here the water drops 1100 feet. The widest waterfall is said to be that at Millstream in northern Queensland. The Blue Mountains have a number of picturesque falls*

MEANDERS: *The great mystery. Both on steep slopes and flat plains, creeks and rivers meander—but why? Science still has no answer to this question*

The largest river, the Murray and its tributaries, drains an immense area of over 400,000 square miles, almost one seventh of Australia, yet the average annual flow is only 12,000,000 acre feet compared with 72,000,000 for the Nile and 725,000,000 for the Yang-tze. Within this average there are wide limits of variability. The Darling River has an average flow of just over 2,000,000 acre feet. This can drop to as low as 1000 and rise to 11,000,000 acre feet. The story is paralleled in most other rivers. However, this is not to say that such rivers have little effect in moulding landscapes today. A sudden flood can move immense amounts of material even in areas where the rainfall is 10 inches or less. Every few years the Trans-Continental Railway line is broken in places by floodwaters along the track. Watercourses in the centre pay tribute to powerful erosional forces.

Underground water

Water that goes underground produces some minor yet interesting landforms. Some streams come out again as springs, or make swamps.

Sometimes when a good waterholding rock like sandstone acts as an aquifer, rain flows steadily down, sandwiched between two impervious rocks. As the water sinks deeper it will build up a great pressure, perhaps being thousands of feet lower than the intake area. Should a well be sunk to tap this layer, water may gush out as an artesian bore. Sometimes when this happens naturally the minerals in the water may build up small hills called mound springs. Such artesian basins are common in Australia and will be discussed later.

Underground water can also destroy. Water is a great solvent, and the oceans of the world contain almost every element, even gold. Water containing carbon dioxide dissolves away lime in the soil. In limestone country spectacular caves may develop. Should a good ventilation develop when a cave breaks through to the surface, then the same lime-charged water will begin to refill the cave with a variety of lime sheets and pillars of fine structures of delicacy and beauty.

Mineral deposits of great value may form through circulating water at depth. A lot of this water forming such deposits comes from rocks deep in the earth's crust. Some deposits form from rainwater from above. The work of the sea as a sculpting force will be discussed in detail in a separate chapter.

The work of ice

In the mountains the snow compacts to ice and a river of ice, a glacier, moves downhill. In its upper reaches the ice freezes around rocks and plucks them away from the hillsides. At a glacier's head a bowl-shaped hollow forms. This is called a "cirque" and resembles an amphitheatre. The glacier carries down with it rocks that fall from the valley sides and at the same time picks up rocks on its bed and grinds away with these. This mixture of material is finally dropped when the ice melts to form terminal moraines or reaches the sea as a glacial till. When hardened this becomes a tillite. The jumble of rocks, often of very different kinds and with little of the wear shown by waterborne material, covers large areas in Australia. In the Great Victoria Desert some years ago we found heaps of these rocks carried there by glaciers that had melted three hundred million years before. Some geologists consider that some of the landforms in these areas still show these ancient glacial influences. The typical valley produced by a glacier is a U rather than a V shape.

GODDARD CREEK: *This river north of Zanthus, Western Australia, is dry for years but occasionally it fills with flooding rains. Then it flows over hundreds of miles of country; sometimes washing away sections of the Trans Line before sinking into the soil. During the dry, the small pools in the stream bed are saltier than the sea*

AROONA DAM COUNTRY: *This valley south of Leigh Creek, South Australia, provides the water supply for the town. Here a broad valley carries the river which is steadily eroding away the hills of the area*

Colour

1

BLUFF KNOLL, *Stirling Ranges, Western Australia*

2

DALE'S GORGE, HAMERSLEYS: *A tiny lost world, a cool and lush oasis in the dry country which surrounds it (Western Australia)*

3

GEIKIE GORGE: *This gorge has been cut by the Fitzroy River, Western Australia, where it eroded an ancient barrier reef. It is about ten miles from Fitzroy Crossing, and is the best known of the scenic attractions of the area. The limestone cliffs are a beautiful sight when mirrored in the permanent pool which runs for miles in the gorge. These waters hold animals such as sawfish and stingrays, which, long cut off from the sea, have managed to survive in a freshwater environment*

4

Top

THE OLGAS: *One of the three famous residuals in the Northern Territory. Ernest Giles the explorer who named it wrote: "The appearance of Mount Olga from this camp is truly wonderful; it displayed to our astonished eyes rounded minarets, giant cupolas, and monstrous domes." Viewed from Ayers Rock at sunset, the Olgas appear a luminous blue against the gold of the setting sun and Giles description of it as a fairytale eastern city is wonderfully apt*

Lower

GLEN HELEN: *The Finke River of the Northern Territory cuts deep gorges in the Macdonnell Ranges. Glen Helen is one of the most famous of these red walled valleys*

44

VALLEY IN THE OLGAS: *In the conglomerate of the Olgas, Northern Territory, steep-sided valleys are common. This is fairly typical of arid land erosion where the height of a mountain diminishes slowly while valleys widen more rapidly*

CANNING STOCK ROUTE WELL: *Deep wells dug in this country provided water for stock moving from Hall's Creek in the Kimberleys to Wiluna in the south. The stock route is no longer used and most of the wells are falling into decay*

DESERT WATERCOURSE: *A torrent when the rains come, dry most of the year (Western Australia)*

RIPPLEMARKED SANDSTONE: *A fossil stream pattern where these ripples in the sand have been preserved from an ancient stream bed (South Australia)*

50

KING RIVER GORGE: *The west coast of Tasmania is wild and beautiful. This steep-sided valley is on the route of the railway from Queenstown to Regatta Point, on Macquarie Harbour. The steep slopes of this country have led to the development of locomotives fitted with cogwheels which fit on racks between the rails to prevent slipping*

GILBERT RIVER: *This river in North Queensland is typical of so many in Australia that run only in the wet season. However, in some there is an underground stream; this runs the whole year round and can be tapped by wells. The dry stream beds make excellent camping places, being both clean and soft to lie on. However, a flash flood upstream may bring down a wall of water that can destroy the camp and drown the campers*

52   ASHBURTON RIVER: *These steep-sided banks pay*
tribute to the rush of water that pours down this river
after cyclonic rains. Between rains it shrinks to a
string of pools (Western Australia)

WINTER SCENE, AUSTRALIAN ALPS: *Even with snow on the ground, running streams keep up their erosive work*

SUMMER SCENE, AUSTRALIAN ALPS: *With summer the snowfields shrink and almost disappear. Layers of red dust appear on the white surface, showing where fine soil from the inland has come to rest (New South Wales)*

GLACIAL ERRATICS: *This large boulder has been dragged along in a glacier, scraping the bed rock. The straight lines gouged in the boulder can be seen. Nearby is a mixture of rocks carried by the glacier and deposited as a moraine when the ice is melted (Western Australia)*

54

5
The work of plants and animals

HERE is a vast and complex topic. In general it can be said that the work of plants is partly destructive in rocky landscapes in terms of rock fracture, mostly constructive in holding the mantle of soil secure, once it has been formed, from wind, river, or sea attack.

Animals are sometimes constructive in terms of work done. Charles Darwin in a classic study of earthworms found that in England with 53,000 worms to the acre the animals brought ten tons of soil to the surface each year. In a field covered with stones, thirty years of steady work buried the stones completely. In the wetter areas of Australia earthworms carry out the same sort of work. In the drier areas the work of converting plant material into soil is done by termites. These insects also add their own clay mounds as a distinctive form to the larger forms of the landscape.

Overgrazing by native animals may have occurred before the coming of man. With the Aborigines came the use of fire as a hunting weapon and slight changes to the landscapes through the destruction of plant cover, allowing erosion forces to work once more. The white man speeded up this process and with him came various animals that often brought disaster. Rabbits both along coastal plains and in the desert have denuded stable dunes and set them on the move once more. On a small scale, grazing by sheep has produced new land patterns in Central Australia and eroded paddocks over much of the coastal regions. In the Australian Alps summer mountain grazing has caused disastrous changes. Some islands have been stripped bare by goats. Man himself, by constructing groynes and similar structures can produce shifts in landforms.

DESERT FIG: *This fig tree grips tightly to a bare rock face and its roots push into cracks, helping break open the rock (Western Australia)*

SYDNEY SANDSTONE: *Once a tree establishes itself in a crevice its roots can help split the bed rock still further*

EROSION: *Trees help bind the soil, but even they are cut away by the sideways swing of this creek (New South Wales)*

Colour
Top
WARRUMBUNGLE MOUNTAINS: *Steep rock formations above a valley of eucalypts (New South Wales)*

Lower
AN ANTICLINE NEAR YASS: *In these low hills the rocks show very plainly the folded nature of the sediments. Here an upfold, or anticline, shows clearly. It is in anticlines such as these, buried deep in the earth, that oil or gas accumulates and can be tapped by drill holes (New South Wales)*

Overleaf
Top
QUEEN VICTORIA SPRING: *In the desert sandhill country, often in hollows, a layer of clay holds water for a time. The sand dune also acts as a reservoir, and this water seeps into shallow wells round the edges of the claypan. This particular waterhole played an important part in the exploration of the western desert (Western Australia)*

Lower
RED LESCHENAULTIA: *The leached sands of the south-west, though deficient in minerals for successful farming, grow a magnificent assemblage of wildflowers, many of them being found only in this area. The leschenaultias include many coloured forms, the most noted being a sky blue (Western Australia)*

56

THE INFLUENCE OF SUNLIGHT: *On this rocky ridge an interesting plant growth has developed. On the northern side, where strong sun beats all day, the Desert Spinifex grows. On the south side, sheltered from the great heat, Mulgas can grow. So aspect affects the weathering of landforms (Western Australia)*

MURRAY RIVER BEDS: *These sandy limestones are little changed from when they were laid down as sediments (South Australia)*

59

FOSSIL ROCK: *This sandy limestone shows a line of shells and shell fragments where the sediment has been laid down under water*

FOSSIL SHELLS: *A sandy limestone with fossil animals embedded in the sand*

GIANT TERMITE MOUND: *A landform created by animals. Millions of termites build these huge cities on northern plains (Northern Territory)*

62   GIANT TERMITES AND BOAB TREE: *These termite mounds combined with grotesque Boabs make an interesting landscape in northwest Australia*

TERMITE MOUNDS: *Tens of thousands of mounds make spectacular landforms near Normanton, North Queensland*

63

THREDBO VILLAGE ON THE CRACKENBACK: *This valley in the Australian Alps, by its straightness, shows the fault line along which the valley river has eroded its valley (New South Wales)*

6
Mountain building

MOST of us remember from our schooldays information about how mountains were formed and the work of erosional tools in levelling them as has just been described. Perhaps a teacher described how layers of sand and mud were deposited in the sea as sediments. Besides these, the bones and outer shells of animals would form huge layers on the sea bottom. In swamps plant remains would accumulate. Over millions of years, huge thicknesses of sediments would develop in this way. Perhaps a teacher pushed a pad between his hands to show how these layers bent into upward folds called anticlines and downward folds called synclines. If he was a very advanced teacher he used flat sheets of coloured plasticene laid on top of each other to represent the layers of silts, sands, lime or plant peats. By using models like this, the folds can be shown in all sorts of variations as saucers or cylinders or as pitching in various directions.

Perhaps—depending on how long ago—you picked up the incorrect idea that these upfolds represent the mountains and the downfolds the valleys. Or in other words when the land rose above the sea its surface was already corrugated. Modern research shows that the actual folding of the rocks is a slow process, which may take millions of years. When uplift does occur it normally comes after the folding is finished. The slope of the land when it comes above the sea will have little to do with the pattern of the folds underneath. Of course when the rivers begin to cut into the folds, their subsequent courses may be affected by the nature of the folds and the kind of rocks they contain.

A weakness in the crust of the earth may cause a crack to develop, and the land on each side of the crack slides. The movement is termed a fault and may be vertical or horizontal or a combination of both. When such a move takes place, perhaps only a few inches, perhaps nearly fifty feet, the land itself shudders and shock waves are sent round the earth, sometimes causing huge landslides, or so-called tidal waves, better termed "tsunamis". Such earthquakes are common and in certain areas to be dreaded. The small movements when repeated over thousands or millions of years can create large effects on landscape, and some faults have been traced for several miles vertically and more than fifty miles horizontally.

Where a whole block of land is lifted, perhaps along one edge only or along several, fault scarps develop. Sometimes parallel faults give us rift valleys. The study of such shiftings of the earth is important to a study of landforms and equally important for those who wish to follow some valuable vein or rock across the line of fault.

Where fractures reach molten rock deep in the earth, or pressures from below produce such fractures, molten rock can reach into surface layers or break through. Volcanoes can create impressive landforms very rapidly. For example one volcano pushed out 100,000 tons of lava a day and in two years pushed up a cone of 150,000,000 tons in weight. In size it was ten miles in diameter and 1500 feet high. Australia has a number of landforms created by volcanic action or lava flows and these will be discussed under the regions.

The scientific detective

Disentangling the story of the rocks and the landforms is like detective work. Just as with crime

LEOPOLD RANGES: *These sedimentary beds of sandstone were crumpled and folded under great heat and pressure changing into quartzites. New beef roads are opening up this country, both for cattle trucks and tourist cars (Western Australia)*

detection, each year sees new tools provided by science to solve the mystery of the past. There are many and varied tools available. From a study of fossils, the remains of plants and animals, much can be learnt of the rocks on the surface. Seismic and other methods allow investigation of deep-seated sediments and their structure. There are even more esoteric methods being developed today.

For example a piece of research from Melbourne could be multiplied in many places. In the Sydney Harbour today there is a shellfish known as the Sydney Cockle. In Port Phillip Bay such cockles are very rare, but in the silts of the West Melbourne swamp the mud is crowded with fossil shells of this cockle. The inference here is that in the times when the silts were being laid down, the waters of Port Phillip Bay were warmer. Under the Spencer Street Bridge 63 feet below the present sea level, a red gum stump was found in its old position of growth. Near it was a peat formed of moss now found on high plains above 4000 feet.

AROONA DAM: *Near the north of the Flinders Range, in South Australia, is the coal mining township of Leigh Creek. About ten miles to the south a dam was built to provide water for the town. This man-made lake and the rugged quartzite hills surrounding it have now become one of the pleasure grounds for the townsfolk. Here the rocks dip steeply into the valley*

This indicates both a period much wetter and cooler than now, and that the Yarra River channel once lay about 60 feet below its present level. Similar results have been found in work on the Swan River channel.

Another important tool in dating deposits up to 40,000 years is known as the radio-active carbon method. This is worked out from an examination of different kinds of carbon found in fossils. Using this tool, the past climate of Melbourne is shown to have been drier and warmer about 4000-6000 years ago. Then the climate became cooler and wetter. Other methods are used to indicate that three ice ages intervened during the last million years. So from an examination of the rocks the geologists can probe farther and farther into the past. However, with deeper insight, the problems become more complex rather than simpler.

BRACHINA GORGE: *The "grain" of the country shows plainly in this picture as the rocks dip steeply into the earth (South Australia)*

KRICHAUFF RANGE: *From the air the "bones" of the country stand out sharply. Tilted quartzite ridges though hard, have been cut by streams feeding into a mainstream system which runs along the grain of the country. In many of the ranges of the Macdonnells, this kind of landscape can be seen (Northern Territory)*

7
This land of Australia

A FLAT COUNTRY, is the general impression Australia gives. Ideal flying country in modern terms, since mountains provide few barriers. Less than 7 per cent of the country is above 2000 feet and the highest mountain barely tops 7000 feet. If we look at other continents of similar size there is a vast difference. The United States for example has nearly half its land above 2000 feet.

However, there are differences in this overall flatness. Broadly speaking there is an eastern line of highlands, a central plain basin and a huge western plateau. The fold mountains so typical of other continents are missing; only just missing since from New Zealand to New Guinea there is a great crescent of mountains. Our mountains are ancient structures, worn down during past ages and lifted again in recent times to provide more modest highlands.

Within this pattern of three simple physiographical features there are other aspects. The Commonwealth Scientific and Industrial Research Organization publication *The Australian Environment* lists the main features as follows:

The Eastern Highlands

From Tasmania to Cape York these stretch in an almost unbroken line. However, since the mountains were formed by warping and faults, movement of the old peneplain has resulted in some smaller plateaus, the best known from the south northward being the Bogong High Plains, the New England Tableland, and the Atherton Plateau.

The sedimentary basins

The Great Artesian Basin covers more than half a million square miles, and to the south of this are the Murray Artesian Basins. To the west is the Eucla Basin, and northwards the Northwest and Desert Basins. There are also coastal basins very widely distributed.

Shatter Belt

In South Australia there is a region known as the Shatter Belt, where block faulting has produced some interesting mountain scenery.

Other features

Smaller plateaus of slightly younger rocks occur, the best known being the Hamersleys in mid-western Australia, the Kimberley Plateau, and the Arnhem Land Plateau.

Sandy deserts

These are a feature of the central desert country and for hundreds of miles long sandridges dominate the countryside. Nearer the coast the red dunes of the desert give way to white sand dunes with a high proportion of lime in the sand.

70

STIRLING RANGES: *Surrounded by farms this national park in Western Australia is important as a sample of the land as it was before the white man came*

WINDJANA GORGE: *Three hundred million years ago, in Western Australia, a huge barrier reef, similar to the Great Barrier Reef flourished here. Today it remains as the Napier and Oscar Ranges. Time has cut fantastic gorges in the once solid reef Windjana is a great gash in the Napier Range, cut by the Lennard River. Three miles long the gorge is flanked by vertical limestone walls up to 300 feet high and with hundreds of caves honeycombing the rocks. Besides its spectacular nature it is also a classic geologic section since it cuts through the ancient Devonian Reef*

ELLEN'S PEAK IN THE STIRLING RANGES: *This mountain rises abruptly from the surrounding plain and looks almost like a backdrop for a stage. It stands etched against the blue sky and the golden-brown of land left behind when a fault dropped away the earth about it. Such a structure is called a "horst". A study of the rocks of the Stirlings shows that the movements must have been fairly complicated to produce the pattern of rocks found there today. It is now one of the best known of Western Australian National Parks, offering magnificent scenery and a fantastic assemblage of wildflowers. Some of the most spectacular of these are confined entirely to these ranges, sometimes to particular peaks*

BLUE LAKE: *The main tourist attraction of southern South Australia is the Blue Lake of Mount Gambier. There are four lakes here, and they lie in the craters of extinct volcanoes. The outlines of these cone-shaped hills and their central craters are still plain to see. Blue Lake has a depth of 226 feet and a crater circumference of three miles. The water area is 176 acres. The most interesting point about the water is its colour change. From December to February the normal dark colour of the water changes to a beautiful turquoise blue.*

The blue colour is something of a mystery. One solution may be that during winter months the surface water becomes cold and shrinks. This makes it denser so it sinks through the less dense water below until it reaches the bottom. This circulation goes on throughout the winter. Aided by strong winter winds and heavy rain it keeps the water constantly disturbed, so the mud is kept in movement and the waters murky. With the coming of summer the surface water becomes warm, expands and is therefore less dense, so it floats on the colder water below. The waters of the lake can become still and the heavier particles of mud settle. Only the finest of silt is left in the water, just enough to diffuse sunlight and give the magnificent blue colour. As the material settles towards autumn, the colour fades. Fine particles in seawater around Broome and Thursday Island give those waters the same exquisite turquoise blue

CHAMBERS PILLAR: *This strange sandstone formation is in the Northern Territory, just over the South Australian border. Ernest Giles described it in this way: "Upon reaching it I found it to be a columnar structure, standing upon a pedestal which is perhaps eighty feet high, and composed of loose white sandstone, having numbers of blocks lying about in all directions. From the centre of the pedestal rises the pillar, composed also of the same kind of rock; at its top and for twenty to thirty feet from its summit the colour of the stone is red . . . The stone is so friable that names can be cut in it to almost any depth with a pocket-knife." From this description it would appear that here is a lone remnant of a mesa in the last stages of decay. The red topping with white rock below is characteristic of these breakaways, with the lower layers leached of minerals*

Colour
Top
SNOWY RIVER: *Large smooth rounded boulders are a tribute to the force of the river when in flood (New South Wales)*

Lower
MILLSTREAM FALLS: *The widest falls in Australia, in North Queensland*

Overleaf
THE AUSTRALIAN ALPS: *Snowdrifts lie piled like sand dunes, with a steep fall to the cirque of Blue Lake. Away from the snowline rugged mountain peaks stretch to the west (New South Wales)*

WARRUMBUNGLE RANGE: *The Warrumbungles have become one of the scenic attractions of New South Wales. Part of the Great Dividing Range and about 60 miles to the north of Dubbo, their peaks reach heights of about 4000 feet. The range is volcanic and the cores of ancient volcanoes still remain, towering as huge monoliths. Mt Wambelong is 4200 feet and tops all the others. However, the best known is the Needle, where the last thousand feet, being of bare rock, provide one of the greatest spectacles the range has to offer*

TUNNEL CREEK: *Tunnel Creek, in Western Australia, literally runs through a mountain. Its half-mile length is broken in the centre where the roof has collapsed and a huge cave entrance leads to the range top. Freshwater pools occur here, and the Aboriginal outlaw Sandamara lived in these hills while he fought his battle with the whites*

THE KING LEOPOLDS: *This range is the southern boundary of the Kimberley Plateau, in Western Australia, and here sandstones, quartzites and conglomerates make up much of the rock of the area. Rivers have cut steep-sided valleys creating one of the most rugged topographies in Australia*

A TYPICAL BREAKAWAY: *The hard red capping of duricrust protects the softer white layers beneath. Part of the hard crust falls away with erosion to tumble to the plain below (Western Australia)*

8
The Great Western Plateau

NINE TENTHS of Western Australia is covered by the plateau, which at times reaches just over 4000 feet, though most of this huge plain is between 1000 and 1500 feet above sea level. Much of this area is built of very ancient rocks, the so-called pre-Cambrian shield of material formed more than five hundred million years ago. This is the stable core of the continent. A wide variety of rocks occur, and down the ages the forces of erosion levelled these off to a huge plain with here and there residual mountains standing higher. In Miocene times the plain was lifted again to become a new plateau. At places the sea terraces formed by the ancient Miocene sea can still be seen, but the major effect of this uplift was that along the edges there were areas which were left behind as lowlands, breaking away from the plateau along huge faults, sometimes in steps, in some cases bending down in what are called monoclinal folds. What is often loosely called the Darling Range is really the Darling Scarp, the edge of the plateau formed when the coastal plain was left behind in the general uplift. On the southern parts of the plateau the most interesting features are the Mount Barren Ranges, Porongorups, and Stirlings. These mountains stand out like islands in the sea of grey-green eucalypt forests and sandplain country that surrounds them. One can easily imagine them as islands in those ancient times when the Miocene sea lapped against the southern edges.

In the locally known "north-west" region, which is really the mid-north of the State, are the Hamersley Ranges. Here the cutting of the river valleys has produced spectacular scenery, and this is prob-ably from a scenic point of view the most exciting part of arid Australia.

In the Kimberleys, similar deep valleys provide magnificent scenery, the best-known area being that of the King Leopold Ranges, where a fault line leads through the Napier and Geikie Ranges down to the lowlands of the Fitzroy River.

Northern Territory

Arnhem Land is very similar to the deeply dissected plateau of the Kimberleys, providing equally magnificent scenery with well-watered valleys. Southwards there are a series of ranges, the best known being those of the Macdonnells, which run east and west and are broken by river gaps, on one of which lies Alice Springs. Then come the big three—Ayers Rock, the Olgas, and Mount Conner. Some of these will be discussed separately, since they feature so large in tourist visits to the Centre.

South Australia

The Musgrave and Everard Ranges link with rugged country in Western Australia. The best known of the ranges are those in the Shatter Belt, which formed the South Australian Highlands. The Mount Lofty Ranges, near Adelaide, run northwards for 400 miles into the spectacular blue hills of the Flinders Ranges.

Queensland

The famous cattle country of the Barkly Tableland and the mining areas of Mount Isa and Cloncurry are part of the eastern edges of the Great Plateau.

BREAKAWAY COUNTRY: *Typical arid scenery. In the breakaways are cool caves where euros can shelter. Flat plains with creeks are surrounded by the plateau which makes the breakaways (Western Australia)*

New South Wales

From the South Australian Highlands a ridge runs into the plateau country of Broken Hill.

Over this huge plateau there are a bewildering variety of landforms and only some of the most striking and unusual will be discussed.

Tent hills or mesas

The common feature through this country is the flat-topped hill. Some hills are residuals of erosion from the original peneplain. Many are younger flat tops when the uplifting of the ancient peneplain started a new cycle of erosion. The old plain in many places had been covered with an armour or cuirass of duricrust. This hard red capping gives the characteristic flavour to the plateau landforms. When it weathers off, and tumbles to the valley below, the expressive term of breakaway is used. Another outback term, "jump up", often refers to the remnant of a breakaway, where a hard ridge still remains.

Gnamma holes

Both in granitic rocks and breakaways occur extraordinary waterholes given the native name of gnamma hole. These rock tanks may hold from a few gallons to thousands of gallons of water. The characteristic shape is that of a narrow-necked bottle, a small entrance leading through the hard capping, then widening out into the water-holding hollow. How these form is something of a mystery. One theory is that an accidental break in the hard cuirass of the surface allows rain and wind to enlarge the hollow in the softer material below. Animals in search of water help by scratching out the soft material, and after many thousands of years the small hollow becomes a sizeable tank. With the coming of the Aborigines these gnamma holes often became very important as staging places when traversing arid country on walkabout. Often the Aborigines covered the holes with rock slabs or bushes to prevent animals falling in and fouling the water.

Salt lakes

A feature of the great plateau country is the salt lakes. The usually accepted theory is that with the lifting and warping of the old plain the river courses were often cut off from the outlets to the sea and ran into huge lakes. Perhaps these were fresh at first, but with the "great dry" of recent times they became salt. The Swan River, on which Perth stands, illustrates the theory. A theory put forward by an early physiographer was that the Avon River once flowed south to an outlet near Albany. With the lifting and tilting of the land it became a sluggish stream pouring its water into a chain of lakes. Along the western edge, the Darling Scarp had rejuvenated small streams flowing westwards, and these began to cut deep gorges through the scarp. It is these deep gorges that provide most of the water storages of the State. However, the Swan River cut back far enough to capture the old south-flowing river, the Avon, and reversed its course. So close to base level is the Avon that one year, at flood time, one of its tributaries, the Mortlock, poured water in so fast that it could not escape downstream, so the Avon River began to flow the wrong way, filling a weir

BREAKAWAY COUNTRY: *A typical rock edge of a breakaway with a hard capping protecting softer rock beneath*

81

CARNARVON JETTY: *Shallow coastlines off the Western Australian coast make good anchorages for ships a problem. Most of the ports on this coast are artificial constructions*

at the town of Northam from the wrong end, the downstream side. A puzzling feature of the salt lake story is that, in general, north of a line running roughly from Shark Bay southeastwards, then turning eastwards about a hundred miles north of Kalgoorlie, the ground water is fresh. South of this line the ground water is salt. The vegetation also shows this change above ground. South of the line the eucalypts are found scattered throughout the country; north of it, eucalypts are found only along watercourses, while mulga takes over as the tree ground cover. So the line has been called the Mulga-Eucalypt Line. Nobody has as yet given any satisfactory explanation of this division.

Where does the salt come from?

Some of course may have been in the soil as a result of its geological history when under the sea. Some also comes from the air. Carried in from the sea by strong winds are tiny salt particles, important perhaps as nuclei on which raindrops can condense. Around Perth at the present time one hundred pounds of salt fall on each acre each year. One hundred and fifty miles to the east at Merredin, this drops to sixteen pounds on each acre each year. This is a pattern to be found the world over, but normally the salt is leached out and taken back to the sea. In Western Australia particularly, the sluggish drainage, the granite shield which does not allow deep penetration of the soil beneath, has created an unusual problem with the salting of cleared land and the formation of new lakes where none occurred before. Nearer the coast these new lakes are usually fresh, but in the wheatbelt they are normally salt.

Basically the rise of water is due to the clearing

WILPENA POUND: *Many legends have risen around this remarkable rock structure in the Flinders Ranges, South Australia. The name was given by early pastoralists, who were struck by the rock enclosure, an ideal place to pound animals. Twenty miles round and with an area of 29 square miles, Wilpena is now a popular tourist spot. Structurally the pound is made of sandstone and is basically a huge hollow in the sandstone beds. The edges of the sandstone make massive rearing cliffs which close the pound on all sides. A river cuts through on the northeast side*

82

RIVER GUMS: *Most of the rivers of Australia are lined with River Gums like these at Wilpena Pound. In dry country a line of trees is sure indication of a creek or river ahead*

of the land of its deep rooted trees and shrubs. Plants such as these act as very efficient water pumps and for hundreds of years have been used to drain swampy land. In the wheatbelt the water table was on the average twenty to thirty feet below the surface and normally this subsoil water was salt. With clearing, the water table lifted to six feet below the surface. An experiment by the C.S.I.R.O. at Griffith was very instructive:

A cylinder of soil a yard in diameter and 13 feet deep was fitted into a steel pipe, closed at the bottom. Water was admitted through the base so that the water table rose to within 3 feet of the surface. After four years salt accumulated in the surface soil and the content went up three times. The surface became dark and greasy and then came the white encrustation typical of salt land, and at this stage no plants can grow. In the West-

MOUNT BARREN: *Surrounded by sandplain, which in the spring and summer is a sea of flowers (Western Australia)*

GNAMMA HOLE IN GRANITE: *A natural rock catchment in desert country*

STANDLEY CHASM: *This gash in the Macdonnell Ranges 30 miles west of Alice Springs was named in honour of the first teacher in the area, Ida Standley. Because of the width of about 20 feet and the height of 500 feet it is only lit directly by the sun at midday. The walls then glow with light*

84

BLUFF KNOLL, STIRLING RANGES: *This peak reaches just over four thousand feet and is the highest in the Stirlings (Western Australia)*

GNAMMA HOLE: *One of the waterholes often found in breakaway country on top of the hard rocks of the plateau*

ern Australian wheatbelt 100,000 acres have been destroyed and a million acres are threatened. The rise of salt is not confined to the Great Plateau but is also a problem in irrigation areas.

As a landform the natural salt lakes are most striking. Usually they are very shallow and remarkably level. For this reason they have become popular for motor car racing. Around the edges of filled lakes is the typical froth associated with salt. This is a quick way of distinguishing salt lakes from freshwater claypans. Also salt quickly causes fine silt particles to settle—one reason why the oceans are so clear. In freshwater claypans the water usually remains completely muddy until the pan finally dries out. Common salt is only one of the minerals found in salt lakes. Another common mineral is gypsum, the raw material used for

DEAD CATTLE: *Claypans often prove traps for thirsty cattle. A small pool of water in the centre of the lake lures the cattle into the soft mud*

making plaster of paris. Known as kopai, it often forms extensive beds, and in this rather porous soil cars often bog.

Once every ten or twenty years, when unusual rains flood the inland, the chains of salt lakes are joined into one long river which flows strongly, sometimes into a final lake, sometimes even reaching one of the seaward-flowing river systems.

SALT LAKE: *The flat clay bed is usually dry. Even when the lake holds water this often moves to different sections depending on the wind direction (Western Australia)*

SALT LAKES: *Rottnest Island near Fremantle is a famous tourist resort, and among its attractions are the numerous salt lakes, sections of the sea cut off by a falling sea level. Some of the lakes are much saltier than the sea and have big concentrations of animals such as brine shrimps that attract abundant bird life*

LAKE COWAN: *Salt lakes such as this are common in the drier areas of Australia. The lake bottoms are both flat and hard most of the time but in flood years may hold water (Western Australia)*

89

DESERT ROAD: *This road to the Warburtons in the mid-east of Western Australia runs through typical outback country. Red sand makes the road bed while all about stretch red sandridges*

FRESHWATER LAKE: *With the clearing of the land and the rising watertable, many lakes appeared in farming country. The trees were soon killed by being continually waterlogged (Western Australia)*

IRON KNOB: *This iron ore deposit on the west side of Spencer Gulf, South Australia, played a big part in the early steel industry*

KATHERINE GORGE: *The sandstone and conglomerates are broken by joints. Along these cracks weathering takes place. The river runs through a deep gorge producing magnificent scenery (Northern Territory)*

ORD RIVER: *In its upper reaches the river passes through the Carr Boyd Range, Western Australia, and here it is intended to make a huge storage dam. This will hold back 3,500,000 acre feet of water, more than seven times the volume of Sydney Harbour*

Colour
Top
SAND BEACHES: *Typical of much of the south and west coasts of Australia are extensive areas of sandy beaches backed by sand dunes*

Lower
COASTAL REEF: *Western coastline with rocks made of dune limestone or aeolianite and protected by wave-cut platform. The outer edge of the platform has a raised rim caused by the greater activity of reef building plants and animals in this zone. Dune limestone usually shows much current bedding, indicating the way in which the winds blew the sand to shape the original moving dunes*

Overleaf
Top
NULLARBOR PLAIN: *Once this area was below the sea, and hundreds of feet of limestone were laid down. The Plain stretches at least a hundred miles to the north of the Trans Line, and about two hundred miles on each side of the Western Australian-South Australian border, with its southern edge fronting the Great Australian Bight in a most striking sea-cliff edge. Most of the plain is treeless, mainly because of the lack of soil cover and the fact that limestone allows the scanty rainfall to penetrate quickly into the rocks out of reach of plant roots*

Lower
EUCLA: *This was once an important place in the Overland Telegraph system, and the beautifully built stone homesteads still stand. However, over-grazing round this Western Australian town caused the sand dunes to move. Today the place has been abandoned, and the small settlement has moved to the high ground of Hampton*

NATIVE DAM: *At the lowest point in natural claypans, Aborigines sometimes made small dams to trap passing rain showers. With the small amount of water saved in this way they could camp in the area for a few weeks and hunt game. When the water dried out they would move on (Western Australia)*

95

COOPER CREEK ENTERS LAKE EYRE: *The long journey ends in a huge inland lake when exceptional rains allow the Cooper flow to bring water along its whole length. Normally such flood waters never reach the journey's end (South Australia)*

LAKE EYRE: *This huge salt lake in South Australia covers some 3000 square miles, and is the drainage basin for half a million square miles of country. However, the rivers like Cooper Creek and the Warburton, though long, run through the dry heart of Australia. It is rare for their floodwaters ever to reach Lake Eyre, though this does happen. In 1950 the whole of the lake filled with water, though the greatest depth was only 12 feet. With an annual evaporation rate of about 100 inches and an annual rainfall of only 5, any water that does flow into the lake soon evaporates. Some parts of the lake are 39 feet below sea level. This fact led to ideas that if only a canal could be cut from the sea to the lake, the presence of water might turn the country into a green and smiling land. Apart from the enormous engineering feat required to cut the canal, there is no evidence that an inland sea would cause an improvement in the rainfall. The Nullarbor Edge and the Great Sandy Desert of Western Australia all abut on oceans without any great improvement in rainfall.*

It is thought that once these lakes were part of a southward flowing river system. Tilting of the land first blocked the river from reaching the sea to form a huge freshwater lake given the name of Lake Dieri. With increasing aridity this huge expanse shrank to form Lakes Blanche, Callabonna, Frome, Gregory, and Eyre

9
The Central Basin

THE second of the main divisions is the Central Basin or lowlands. Just as the Great Plateau has been above the sea for hundreds of millions of years, the huge central sedimentary basin has apparently always been a low-lying area. Often invaded by the sea and more recently an area of huge freshwater lakes with a rich marsupial fauna, the central area, though now much drier, still holds huge quantities of water in artesian form. It is best here to consider also the smaller sedimentary basins.

Great Artesian Basin

This is a huge area of 550,000 square miles and the largest of the 1,000,000 square miles of Australian artesian basins. Such basins, if of the classical type are shaped like a saucer or in other words a synclinal type of structure. Lining the bottom of the saucer must be rock beds that will not allow water to penetrate, impervious beds like shales. Then there must be overlying beds that hold water well—aquifers such as sandstones. Above this, there must be a layer of impervious beds once more, so that the water coming in at the edge of the saucer flows down as though in a pipe and cannot escape. At the bottom of the basin it remains under continuous pressure from the water higher up. In Australia all the basins are modified in other ways, usually being one half a basin. In other words the water coming in at the high point of the saucer flows steadily down until finally it escapes through some natural outlet, usually under the sea.

In the Great Artesian Basin the intake beds are along the western edge of the Eastern Highlands, an area of high rainfall. The rocks are mainly between 1000 and 2000 feet above sea level. The floor of ancient rocks is not perfectly even and two ridges break up the basin into three parts. The northern basin slopes away to the Gulf of Carpentaria, and the natural outlet is on the sea bed there. It is thought that in the central part of the basin the deepest part is 7000 feet below sea level. This means that water there is perhaps as much as 9000 feet below the level of intake and so must be under a tremendous pressure. Any break in the top rock layer which holds this water captive means it flows upwards either as a natural or artificial artesian outlet.

Natural artesian wells sometimes have mound springs round them, where minerals in solution are deposited when the water evaporates at the surface. North-eastern South Australia has a large number of these. Sometimes the water comes up almost boiling, and at Normanton the flow is turned into a fountain which serves two purposes —one aesthetic and the other practical, to cool the water before it flows into the town public swimming pool and hot shower system.

This huge underground reservoir has meant a great deal to the pastoral industry. The deepest water-bearing layer that has been tapped is 6000 feet below the surface, and with 2500 artesian bores there has been some decline in output. A 1945 estimate was 300,000,000 gallons a day for the whole basin. However, 700 bores in Queensland have stopped flowing and those nearest the intake beds are slowing down.

Murray Artesian Basin

This basin in lower New South Wales, Victoria

and South Australia has a number of bores sunk in it, but most tap sub-artesian supplies only. On the western edge along the South Australian coastline sand dune ridges have been thrown up and many coastal lakes occur there.

Eucla Basin

This water lies under the famous Nullarbor Plain. This huge area of limestone soaks up water as soon as it falls, and so lacks rivers. The lack of soils means that only small plants can grow except in occasional hollows where soil collects. These are locally called "dongas" and often carry medium sized trees such as False Sandalwood and Native Pittosporum. On the southern edge of the Nullarbor is a steep cliff, believed to be part of a fault line that continues inland to make the Hampton Range. The lack of surface erosion by rivers and constant battering of the sea has kept the shorelines as a steep cliff. However, in the limestone are numbers of sink holes leading to caverns in the rock. All these are caused by chemical weathering where rain water charged with carbon dioxide is acid enough to dissolve the lime. Huge caves like Koonalda also have large lakes inside them. The Koonalda lake is used as a source of pastoral water. Another interesting feature of the area are the blowholes where at certain times of the day air rushes out with tremendous violence. Apparently this is caused by heating of the air in the cavern and its expanding and flowing out. During cooler periods the air flows in again.

To the north, sandridge country overlies the Nullarbor limestone. Along the northern edge bores sunk into the basin are producing much fresher water than those nearer the coast. Also still farther north other basins occur in the sandridge country. Here can be found outcrops of rocks deposited by glaciers that moved through the country three hundred million years ago. Some of the erratics carried by the ice show the straight grooves scratched in them when they were locked in the glacier. Drilling for oil is being carried out in this basin area.

On the Western Australian coast are three more basins.

Coastal Plain

The plain on which Perth lies is a most interesting feature. Recent work seems to indicate that there are possibly 40,000 feet of sediments underlying the area before the ancient shield bedrock is reached. The plain lies along the scarp, and apparently the land was either faulted or warped down to form a basin in which sediments have been deposited for many hundreds of millions of years.

Northwest and Desert Basins

The coastal plain continues northwards to form two other major basins, the Northwest and Desert Basins. All three have been drilled for oil and all yield excellent artesian water. Some of the limestones in the Cape Range area of the Northwest Basin have been eroded away to make spectacular gorges, and the Desert Basin is a forbidding region of sand dunes. However, adventurous parties of naturalists and better-organized groups of mineral and oil exploration parties are rapidly penetrating much of this country, which until twenty years ago was almost unknown territory to the white man.

SAND DUNE COUNTRY NORTH OF THE FINKE RIVER: *During the "great dry", half a million square miles of sandridge country was created. Probably there was always a central desert area but in this period of aridity it enlarged greatly. These parallel dunes are often up to sixty feet in height and run for hundreds of miles about a quarter of a mile apart*

98

SINKHOLE: *Limestone country often has sinkholes where acid rain water has dissolved away the lime and leads into large caverns below the surface*

ORGAN PIPES: *Here a group of stalactites create a beautiful effect. Often lakes form on the floors of caves. Fossil bones of animals may be found in the soil of the floors, where these creatures came to hide or feed (Augusta, Western Australia)*

MAMMOTH CAVE: *From the ceiling delicate stalactites grow downwards, while from the floor massive stalagmites build up. Should these join a pillar results* (*Margaret River, Western Australia*)

KOONALDA CAVE ENTRANCE: *This cave in the Nullarbor Plain contains a lake ninety feet deep lying in a huge cavern 300 feet long and 200 feet wide*

INLAND RIVER: *This aerial photo of the Darling River flowing through western plains gives an excellent example of the meandering course, the tree-lined nature of the stream and the numerous cut off lakes or billabongs that occur in the area. In flood times the water overflows its banks for miles and fills large lakes nearby*

MURRAY RIVER, SOUTH-EAST OF EUSTON: *Australia's largest river winds its way leisurely to the sea. This river drains an area of about four hundred thousand square miles*

THE THREE SISTERS: *Here erosion has created pinnacles of rock in the Hawkesbury sandstone. The slightly dust-filled air creating a blue haze is typical of Australian scenery (New South Wales)*

10
The Eastern Highlands

THIS is a huge area stretching from Cape York southwards to Victoria and Tasmania. Broadly speaking it can be described as a huge plateau sloping fairly gently to the west and more steeply to the east. At times it reaches the coast, at times is distant from it. The plateau in southern Queensland is 400 miles wide, but narrows elsewhere. The rivers have carved deep gorges in this plateau, created isolated areas of high land, locally given names as separate ranges, and some of the higher peaks are well known. Mount Bartle Frere reaches a height of 5287 feet. The Glasshouse Mountains are features near Brisbane.

In New South Wales the New England Plateau is part of the highlands, and these extend southwards towards Sydney. As with other areas dissec-

tion by rivers has given rugged mountain scenery including the famed Blue Mountains. Then comes the highest section of the Eastern Highlands, in the Australian Alps. Mount Kosciusko at 7316 feet is the highest point in Australia.

The highlands of Victoria are a divide between plains to the north and lowlands to the south. The spectacular high points are in the Australian Alps, Mount Bogong topping 6516 feet.

Tasmania is half highland over 2000 feet. Rising above the plateau are ranges reaching over 5000 feet. The best known is the Cradle Mountain. These uplands show much more the work of ice, and are discussed in the next section. In the northeast, ice also sculpted the areas round Mount Barrow and Ben Lomond.

MOUNT LINDESAY: *This peak near the New South Wales-Queensland border is part of the McPherson Range and rises to a height of 4064 feet. Like the Glasshouse Mountains farther north it is part of an old volcanic cone*

SOUTH HEAD: *Sydney has a world-famous harbour and the massive, sandstone headlands that guard the entrance are repeated in great variety to give the area around Sydney its rugged beauty. The very harshness of the sandstone, which weathers to a barren sandy soil, saved the country round the capital from development for farming. As a result the original bush can be seen within a few miles of the city and lyrebirds still nest there. Most of the rocks now on the surface were laid down in a huge lake, for most of its time a freshwater one. Here huge beds of sand and clay were laid down. With earth movements, the sands became sandstone and the clays, shale. The sandstone, hard and resistant, makes the high cliffs already mentioned. The shales weather to clay soils, best seen from Ryde to Pennant Hills. Into these gently folded beds came intrusions of volcanic rocks, dolerites, and more finely grained basalts. These volcanic rocks, if they push between old beds to form layers, are called dykes. Long Reef is a good example of one dyke of basalt. Not always do these basalts last better than the surrounding rocks. Sometimes they weather to soft clay and only show their presence by hollows in the harder sandstone.*

This whole land surface was first raised, then reduced to a plain. Possibly a humid tropical climate laid down the superficial duricrust described elsewhere. Then came the huge rise of a million years ago named the Kosciusko Uplift. The sluggish rivers, rejuvenated, began to cut deep gorges in the old plain, which was now a plateau once more. This is a pattern repeated through the highlands of Australia.

With the melting of much of the ice of the more recent ice ages, the valleys flooded to form the estuaries and inlets, the most famous of which is Port Jackson, but there is too the equally beautiful Broken Bay.

However, this rise in sea level was not continuous. A slight retreat of the sea during a minor ice age meant that sandy beaches were exposed above the sea. Winds would soon heap this exposed sand into ridges and form dunes such as those found at Botany Bay. Even more important, the ridges became high enough to remain dry land when the sea returned, and old islands were kept linked with the mainland. Barrenjoey is a good example of a tied island, sometimes called a tombolo

104

TOWER HILL: *A volcano may have only a small crater, but sometimes craters are enlarged and given the special name of caldera. Sometimes the larger size may be caused by a terrific explosion blowing away the top of the crater, or the walls of the cone may become undermined, or perhaps the molten lava withdraws down the pipe from which it originally came to build the cone. Tower Hill, in Victoria, is such an ancient volcano, and is now a sanctuary. It is near the town of Warrnambool. The original caldera lake has shrunk somewhat. Inside the crater are a number of smaller cones, formed of pieces of lava termed scoria. Very aptly a caldera with a number of inner cones like this is known as a "nested caldera"*

LION ISLAND: *Where the Hawkesbury enters the sea. This picture of Broken Bay is taken from West Head*

BYRON BAY: *A sheltered sandy beach develops between headlands at this eastern-most point on the coast of New South Wales*

THE GRAMPIANS: *This is the western end of the Great Dividing Range or Eastern Highlands. This range of mountains is one of the popular tourist resorts of Victoria. The sandstone and granite that make up the ranges have worn away into picturesque rugged country*

BROWN COAL SEAMS: *These lignites or brown coals of Victoria were laid down in swamps in estuaries; and in some places thicknesses of five hundred feet have been produced. As a fuel the deposits are of great importance. This picture shows the sediments in one of the open cuts*

MOUNT BOGONG: *The highest point in Victoria, this mountain lies in the Australian Alps and is the centre of a thriving winter tourist area based on snow sports and a summer tourist interest of bush-walking and scenery. Aborigines once came here in summer to feast on the Bogong Moths*

BLUE LAKE: *This lake near Mount Kosciusko is one of several on a popular walk from Mount Kosciusko to Charlotte's Pass. All are excellent examples of glacial lakes dammed by moraines. These lakes were gouged out by glaciers. In the whole area are many landforms typical of glaciated valleys*

II
The Australian Alps
and the Tasmanian Highlands

ALTHOUGH Australians are well aware of the huge area covered by snow, overseas visitors rarely know of this. More skiing slopes than are to be found in Switzerland is one of the boasts of winter sportsmen who enjoy the Snowy Mountains in winter. Dr A. B. Costin, in more scientific fashion, lists the high mountain scenery of Australia as follows: The limit of the high mountain is the limit of the winter snowline. The actual height above sea level depends both on aspect and latitude. In Tasmania this is 3000 feet, in Victoria about 4500 feet, and in New South Wales and the Australian Capital Territory it varies from 5000 to 5500 feet. The grand total is about 2000 square miles on the mainland and another 2500 square miles in Tasmania.

The high mountain country has rather unusual features. Dr Costin in his analysis of the high mountains says that the Tasmanian country tends to resemble British highland. In the Australian Alps there has been a less severe glaciation, the slopes are less and the climate has led to a strong development of soil, so these are soil mountains. But Dr Costin warns that this very uniqueness has its dangers. Each day there may be a change in temperature of fifty degrees. Summer storms bring violent rainfall, so there is danger to the stability of soils. When to this inherent danger was added increasing fire and intensive grazing the result was inevitable. Professor W. R. Browne has written that in many places two feet of soil cover has disappeared through sheet erosion. In the nick of time the New South Wales Government has set aside 1,300,000 acres as a National Park. In the highest portions plans are being made to set aside 98 square miles as a primitive area.

This unique area contains excellent samples of ice erosion such as cirques and glaciated valleys, and it also contains most interesting deposits including moraines and lake deposits, as well as other deposits on slopes. Here there lies, available for study, a "book" that may reveal the history of our planet during the last million years. Only recently have we begun to find the "Rosetta Stones" that allow us to interpret the story. However, there is steady pressure to use the primitive area for other purposes, both for recreation and for industry in terms of a development of the Snowy Mountains Hydro-electric Scheme. It would be a tragedy if shortsightedness should be allowed to destroy this unique landform.

Considered as a whole, this area of high mountains is a place of fairly ancient rocks. One of the features of the making of eastern Australia was a huge trough into which erosion of the land poured material. This trough is known as the Tasman Geosyncline, and it was not just a matter of steady filling, since three times it rose and fell. Not only beds of silt and lime were laid down in this ancient sea. Igneous rocks were injected into the folds, and among these are the granites, which make the land features in many places, including the summit of Kosciusko itself.

Finally just under three hundred million years ago the land rose from the sea for the last time. Down the ages the mountains were reduced to a peneplain with a few higher places showing where more resistant rocks had worn more slowly. By this time the old silts had become slates, the sands, quartzite.

Then some thirty million years ago the plain was lifted once more in a series of movements that

AUSTRALIAN ALPS IN WINTER: *The high mountains in winter present scenes of breathtaking beauty though the present snow has little influence in shaping the landforms to be seen here today*

MOUNT WELLINGTON: *This igneous rock cooled quickly and hence is fine grained and columnar (Tasmania)*

Colour

PORT CAMPBELL: *Some of the most spectacular and beautiful coastal scenery in Victoria occurs along the coast east of Port Campbell. Here hundred-foot-high winter waves batter at soft marine sediments, and by differential erosion have been created a remarkable series of landforms. London Bridge is an arch still joined to the mainland. With further wave action island arches may finally become isolated as island peaks, called "stacks". With more erosion these melt away until only a backward movement of a wave reveals a platform below the water. This is cut away further until it disappears from sight*

Overleaf
Top
GREEN ISLAND: *This coral cay about 16 miles from Cairns, Queensland, attracts holiday-makers. The water over the coral sand is crystal-clear*

Lower
A CORAL REEF AT LOW TIDE: *A few times each year combinations of sun and moon positions provide extreme tidal ranges, and then extensive reefs appear above water. Most coral soon dies on exposure, so coral reefs flourish only below low water mark*

PORT DAVEY: *This harbour about fifty miles south of Hobart is claimed to be Australia's only fiord, a valley sculpted by ice and then drowned by the sea. However, recent work indicates it has no glacial features*

also raised the Great Dividing Range. It was not just a once and for all movement but a series of steps, until about a million years ago came the biggest of them all. This has been named the Kosciusko Uplift. The old plain once worn down to near sea level had been raised high above the sea as a plateau. The slow-moving rivers ran fast once more and their valleys began to bite into the plain. During the long period described, flows of basalt had filled the old valleys and produced a new landscape. Now the remnants of these lava flows withstood much of the gnawing and battering of the rivers.

The visitor to Kosciusko can see all this laid out before him as he ascends the highest point.

The road up which he drives in comfort is a gentle slope, a tribute to the plateau top. At the peak of Mount Kosciusko, on every side stretches a skyline that shows the old level plain on which he now stands. In travelling across the mountain area there is plenty of evidence of the huge uplift where step faults are on the boundary of the old plateau. The paths of the rivers often show these fault lines, and Crackenback in its straight course shows one huge break in the surface. Even the path of the road to the summit seems to reveal a similar fault line.

With the Kosciusko Uplift came the immediate beginning of a redressing of the balance, and rivers like the Snowy, Crackenback and Tumut have cut great gorges into the old plateau. The maze of valleys produces one of the most impressive spectacles of mountain scenery to be found in Australia.

However, the last million years added a new

113

feature, the glacial landscape. In Tasmania the effect was the greatest. Here an ice sheet perhaps some 2000 feet thick covered 4000 square miles and affected three times as much country. Today the effect of that ice can be seen over much of Tasmania. Swampy plains pay tribute to the efficient way in which deposits from glaciers dammed up the water, and such places as Lake St Clair show where much greater depths of water were ponded by such moraines.

Both here and in the Australian Alps there is plenty of evidence of this glaciation. There were at least three ice ages during the last million years. First came a huge ice sheet that ground away the ridges and when it finally retreated left behind much rock debris as moraines. Then came another ice age about 100,000 years ago and this time glaciers moved down the valleys, rounding off the V shape into the U shape typical of ice action. At the beginning of these rivers of ice, formed the cirques, now a feature of the area. Then, quite recently, only twenty thousand years ago, a smaller series of glaciers continued the work. There are a large number of cirques in the area and two well-known ones are Blue Lake and Club Lake, where moraines have dammed the basin. In other places the glaciers scooped hollows out in the valleys, and some of these are now filled with water, as with Lake Albina.

CRATER LAKE, CRADLE MOUNTAIN, BARN BLUFF: *This shows the central mountain area of Tasmania where both peaks are over 5000 feet. Barn Bluff reaches 5114 feet. Cradle Mountain-Lake St Clair area is an important national park, and this landscape is an excellent example of landforms sculpted by ice. The dolerite of Cradle Mountain has been eroded into a cirque where the glaciers have gouged out these amphitheatres. Crater Lake is a glacier lake formed in the valley and dammed by a moraine*

12
The sea and its work

WE HAVE already seen how the relative levels of land and sea can change either by an upheaving of the land or its dropping into troughs under the sea. These movements may take place dramatically in short periods, but normally more slowly over millions of years. There is another change that can come from the melting of the ice on the land, which raises the sea level; or the locking up of water in the form of land ice or snow when an ice age develops, which drops the sea level. The varying changes ice ages have produced on the shoreline of Australia make a fascinating study, and something of its variety has already been shown. The presence of fossils in rocks high on a mountain is dramatic evidence of a sea-level shift. Most of the sediments have been laid down under water. Even in the most ancient western shield, many of the metamorphic rocks were once sediments formed in seas of hundreds of millions and even thousands of millions of years ago.

However, most interesting in a study of present landforms is the recent history of our coastline. In the discussion that follows it must be remembered that a great deal of research is going on at present, and our present ideas may need to be modified with new knowledge. However, broadly it has been established that during the last million years there have been four main ice ages separated by three warmer periods. The first glacial phase is thought to have started 600,000 years ago, the second 480,000 years ago. The third came at 240,000 years and the last at 120,000 years. Then some 20,000 years ago the earth began to warm up once more. This is the period when it is thought the Aborigines came to Australia. Even today the

retreat of glaciers indicates that this warming up is still going on, and some scientists estimate that the sea has risen four inches during the last hundred years.

When we speak of glacial phases and warm periods this does not mean that there was a steady swing from one to the other. In the main movements there would be minor swings backwards and forwards, and some of these show in the landforms we can see along the coast today.

What effect did these ice-age sea-level changes have on Australian landforms? Most scientific workers think that some 6000 years ago the sea reached its present level, rising steadily from the lower levels produced by the last glacial phase. The rivers and shores that had vigorously cut back into the land now became drowned, and this gives the characteristic pattern to the coastline we see today. Minor oscillations in sea level are believed to have produced some interesting features of sea cliffs. For example, at Safety Bay near Fremantle, Western Australia, a long low jetty of rock pushes into the sea. This jetty is today ten feet above the low water mark, and where it meets the limestone cliffs an old beach can be seen plastered on its surface. Here are cemented a collection of sand, pebbles, and shells. Not so well shown are platforms about five to six and two to three feet above low water mark. These three levels are thought to be remnants left behind by the sea as it retreated from higher levels. This place is particularly interesting to geologists, and has become a mecca for scientific visitors. The shells on this beach terrace have been found to be about 5000 years old, and since then, it would seem that the sea has been falling to its present level. Since this part of

POTHOLES: *Waves washing against this limestone platform move the pebbles that cut potholes in the hard rock (Tasmania)*

Australia is a stable area, it presents what seems to be reliable evidence. Yet always at the back of one's mind must be kept the thought—perhaps the land moved as well.

The tools used by the sea

What are the weapons nature uses to shape the coastline? Obviously, ordinary weathering attacks the rocks of the coastline, as it does the rocks inland. These become pitted through chemical action, and the strong sea winds can scour away the debris. In addition, the drying effect of these winds may mean there is less chance for vegetation to grow and protect the rocks from destruction. Yet plants are adaptable and sea rocket, sea spinifex, sea spinach, and mangroves have be-

come adjusted to this harsh environment, holding the sand firmly in place, or clinging to rocks splashed by spray. Mangroves have even invaded the ocean with tough roots firmly anchored in sea mud. People of some parts of the world deliberately plant them to stop marine erosion. In sandier zones beach she-oaks, pandanus, and tea-trees also act as soil binders.

It is therefore waves which act as the great shapers of coastlines. A few minutes' study of wave motion will show that not only the outer coast is affected by waves. Waves can bend round headlands and though reduced in size, still wear away at sheltered bays. Massive cliffs disappear before such attacks, and nowhere in the world can erosion be seen more dramatically than when a winter storm is battering at a rockbound coast. A three-ton block may be tossed over a twenty-foot-high wall. Lighthouses 200 feet above the sea may be damaged by violent waves. Under the ocean the wave effects can be felt to the outer limits of the continental shelf, 600 feet below the sea surface. To give some idea of the force exerted by a wave, it has been found that in severe storms this may reach pressures of 6000 pounds to the square foot. Such a force can move stones weighing 250 tons. Mermaid Rock near Bondi, New South Wales, is a good example. Obviously enough sand and boulders thrown about by wave motion act as battering rams to undercut cliffs and bring them down. Then the backwash of the waves removes the spoil into deeper water.

There is another effect caused by air under pressure being forced into cracks. When the wave retreats the air moves out again under reduced pressure and helps fracture the rock.

Besides the backwash effect, currents and tidal movement will also shift broken off fragments of the coast. In the Kimberleys and also round Thursday Island tidal currents are so powerful that the water becomes muddied with the material being carried. Pearl divers do not work during periods of spring tides because of the murkiness of the water.

Deep below the surface sea currents help with sea-bed erosion.

Building up

The spoil from the coast may be spread over the continental shelf and lost to view until later uplift brings it above the sea once more. Sand and mud become mixed with deposits produced by the dead bodies of animals and plants. However, above the sea there can be many landforms produced by the combined effects of the shape of the coastline, the action of waves, the direction of the wind, and the movements of sea currents.

Cliffs

The coastline at Port Campbell with its popular names of London Bridge and the Twelve Apostles shows stacks and other forms produced by wave erosion. Here the marine sediments lie in horizon-tal layers. A temporary bridge may remain because some layers are harder than others, but gradually all disappear under the movement of the waves. Around Sydney similar steep cliffs front the open ocean, though inside the estuary the slopes tend to be more gentle, since here the waves move more slowly and the land erosion is able to keep pace with the work of the sea.

The notch and visor

An interesting type of shore platform developed on limestone coasts shows a low water mark platform. On its outer edge it often has a raised rim probably because here plants and animals obtain plenty of oxygen and food from the stir of the waves. Behind this raised rim, small pools often collect. Then the platform rises slowly towards the cliff. The cliff often shows what is called a "notch", overhung by a "visor", as used by knights of old in their helmets. Waves and spray have helped make this particular shape. Yet for the specialist there are still teasing problems to be solved. Some of the solutions are most elegant and it is well worthwhile reading a few of the standard textbooks to get some idea of how what looks simple, may be extremely complex.

Plunging cliffs

Where cliffs are made of various tough rocks like granite or gneiss, there may be no shore platforms built up at all but the rocks slide smoothly below the sea. These are dangerous cliffs for fishermen, for the very smoothness of the rocks makes it possible for a man to be swept away by a wave, with no chance of climbing out again. The nearest beach may be several miles away.

Beaches

Sandy beaches may collect between rocky headlands or may run for many hundreds of miles. When waves strike a sand beach at an angle the last few yards of water movement carry sand and pebbles along the beach in the direction of the wave front. Though the water may come in at an angle, it runs out again as backwash at right angles to the beach. Then the sand is picked up once more by the next wave and pushed a little farther

EAGLEHAWK NECK: *A number of interesting land-forms have been created here by wave erosion. Near this spot is the blowhole where wave action sometimes produces spectacular displays of the power of the sea (Tasmania)*

TESSELLATED PAVEMENTS: *A famous landmark on the east coast of Tasmania. Joints in the fine sandstone give a remarkable effect of artificially constructed pavements*

along. So the sand moves in zigzag fashion along the beach front in the direction of the prevailing wind. Sometimes with changes in wind direction in winter and summer as on the south-west coast of Western Australia the sand moved one way by winter waves is returned by summer ones. When man interferes by building a harbour or groyne, the sand may be held in one place, a large beach developing at the expense of sand robbed from a beach nearby. Leighton Beach north of Fremantle is believed to have been created by the effects of the moles built to protect the harbour. In America new sand is often brought in to preserve beaches that are important tourist attractions. Intense research is being carried out to try to avoid such problems. Models of coastal sections are made and in special tanks all the conditions along the coast are reproduced to find out rapidly what can happen if certain headlands are reshaped or new groynes built.

Wave action may produce long spits of sand, and with the passage of time create freshwater lakes behind them. Sometimes these form bars across river mouths. Occasionally off-shore islands are tied to the mainland by a sandspit, perhaps only a winter or a summer feature. Sometimes such spits become permanent, as with Barrenjoey and the Wilson's Promontory granite island. These tied islands are sometimes called tombolos.

When the seabed slope is gentle and the waves break a long way out, a sand bar will form, but this moves slowly in-shore as waves push sand off the crest into the landward side of the bar.

Beach Mining

The careful sorting action of the waves has often created rich deposits of denser minerals such as rutile and zircon. Along the east coast one of the major sources is believed to be the New England Plateau, and erosion brought down the minerals, among other spoil, to be spread by wave action along beaches of the east coast. In the south-west of Western Australia similar deposits occur. In recent years the activities of mining companies have threatened coastal areas that were once thought to be safe from development. One naturalist has even coined the phrase "the thousand-mile desert" to describe the area between Sydney and Rockhampton if the mining companies are not brought under control. The unique complex of plants and animals that have been built up on these sand deposits, once destroyed, are gone forever. This is not just a dog in the manger attitude. Most conservationists are satisfied so long as adequate samples of the coastline are preserved for national parks. It is also essential that once a beach has been mined the companies should be obliged to restore it to a pleasant place once more under the instruction of a government-appointed landscape architect. At present, only near settled areas does popular indignation force the companies to remove the havoc their mining operations has produced.

Sand Dunes

These have been discussed in connection with the sandridge deserts of Australia, but sand dunes are found as important landforms along many coastlines. Because the bulk of the population lives near the coast or finds a large part of its recreation in or near the sea, human pressure has increased considerably on this landform. When sea levels were lower than they are today extensive areas of sand would have been exposed, and under the influence of winds these have been heaped up inland. In addition to the increase in amount of sand available to the wind, there was also a drying out of the continent to increase the influence of wind.

It is extraordinarily interesting to watch how rapidly vegetation advances to stabilize a newly formed dune. The pioneer plants are well fitted by large root systems to resist being blown away and to tap the water held in the dune sand. Their leaves are reduced or hairy, to cut down water loss, and growing as mats close to the ground, they avoid the worst effects of the wind.

Even before the white man, however, there were often "blowouts" where the wind won the battle and the sand began to move. Possibly such blowouts were due to accidental fires or deliberate ones created by the Aborigines. A path used continually will initiate a blowout. In one spot often used by naturalists for a study area in the past, and kept under continual observation, a tourist track is now about twelve feet below the old dune level, because of a blowout. Overgrazing by stock such as goats, camels, and sheep, plus the added effects of rabbits has often caused sand movements on a large scale. In many places, the dunes with their attendant plant and animal life are balanced on a razor's edge. Any undue pressure may mean either direct or indirect swings of the balance in favour of sand movement.

Behind dunes, interdunal lakes may occur, often with only a thin layer of impervious material to hold the water. Again any interference with the floor will cause the lake to disappear. Other odd and unusual occurrences along sea coasts are the large kitchen middens of sea shells associated with feastings by the Aborigines over many generations.

Another most bizarre accumulation of broken shells, well above high tide line and often found on rocky platforms along the southern coastline, appears where these rocks have been used as an anvil by seabirds. The Pacific Gull has a habit of picking up heavy shellfish from off-shore reefs, then flying above a rock platform. The shell is dropped from a height of about twenty feet and shatters on the rock below, where the bird can then enjoy the flesh, leaving behind the shell fragments. Such a collection is a potential deception for geologists in the years to come who might be puzzled by apparent beach debris well away from and above sea level.

Drowned Valleys

With the rising of the sea much of the Australian coastline shows examples of drowned valleys. These are often called rias, though some text books confine the term ria to a drowned valley that is linked with the rock structure running across a coastline. The coast near Yampi shows typical rias of this sort following the "grain" of the country. However, if we accept a wider use of the term, then Port Jackson is a magnificent example of this landform.

Estuaries

There is a good deal of overlap in most scientific terms, and they must always be accepted as convenient boxes for classification with some forms hanging rather untidily over the edge. For example if we accept that an estuary is a river mouth considerably influenced by tidal effects in terms of salt and fresh water, and with a funnel shaped opening pointing to the sea, we may have difficulties separating rias from estuaries. Broken Bay, New South Wales, is a halfway type, while the Swan River, Western Australia, is a typical estuary.

Lagoons

With a diminishing rainfall an estuary might gradually become cut off from the sea by a sand bar and become an estuarine lagoon. In Western Aus-

WEST COAST, TASMANIA: *Sea erosion on a rugged coast showing the cliffs with the highlands behind*

MANGROVES: *The stilt-like roots of this mangrove help bind the mud firm against the effect of tides and waves (Queensland)*

MANGROVES: *A belt of mangroves grows in the mud of this bay near Cooktown, Queensland. These trees are efficient soilbinders. "Mangrove" is a term used not for a single kind of tree but for an association of trees growing along muddy shores*

tralia many sand bars occur, and only very rarely do the rivers break through these. Lagoons can be formed in other ways, and they are a common feature of the coastline.

Deltas

These have already been described. Classic deltas are missing from Australia, since the rivers are still at work filling in drowned valleys caused by the rising sea level. Australian authorities mention how the largest river system in Australia—the Murray-Darling system—has not yet managed to fill the lagoons of Lake Alexandrina and Lake Albert which lie near the entrance. However, the best examples of delta can be seen in rivers running into lakes or bays, as with the Yarra in Port Phillip Bay.

GREAT AUSTRALIAN BIGHT: *Near Koonalda the Eyre Highway passes close to the Bight, and a magnificent view of these great sea cliffs can be obtained by a detour of about ten miles. It is well worth the effort, for this is one of the most spectacular landforms in Australia*

123

THE NOTCH AND VISOR: *This is a characteristic shape produced by wave and splash erosion. As the notch deepens, the visor gradually falls in, so keeping the shape constant*

MOONAHS ON SAND DUNES: *This coastal tea-tree helps hold firm the coastal sand dunes from erosion by the wind (Western Australia)*

SEA SPINIFEX: *This is one of the plant pioneers that move onto newly emerged sand and hold it firm (Western Australia)*

SHELLFISH ANVIL: *Pacific Gulls drop living shellfish on to rocks like these to shatter the armour so they can feed on the mollusc inside. Such collections of shell debris may be many feet above sea level (Tasmania)*

BARRENJOEY, NORTH OF SYDNEY: *From the air it is plain to see how the one-time island of Barrenjoey has been tied to the mainland by a sandspit*

125

FRETTED ROCK: *Coastal limestone frets into strange shapes as shown on this beach in Port Phillip Bay (Victoria)*

SAND DUNE ROCK: *The influence of acid rain water in dissolving lime and then redepositing it along certain layers, creates a rock called dune limestone, or aeolianite. This hard layer was formed over a period of twenty years in a sand dune near Perth. Shell fragments have been cemented into soft rock under the influence of rain water, trickling down the old dune slope (Western Australia)*

13
Coral reefs and islands

CORAL ISLANDS are romantic places, and Australia is fortunate to possess so many. Everybody has heard of the Great Barrier Reef, which stretches for twelve hundred miles from Lady Elliott Island in the south to Torres Strait in the north, and which encloses eighty thousand square miles of ocean. As a landform it is insignificant, since its great bulk lies below the sea. Only if the waters of the Pacific retreated would its immensity be seen. In the Kimberleys an ancient coral reef, now a mountain range, gives some concept of what it would look like.

Coral reefs are not confined to the Queensland coastline. They are found around northern Australia and south along the west coast to the Abrolhos Islands near Geraldton. Reefs are found farther south, but the growths are small. Solitary corals occur in all oceans of the world.

The coral polyps, which build up these reefs, flourish in warm, clear waters. Since part of their oxygen supply comes from simple marine plants called algae growing in their tissues, they cannot grow strongly below two hundred feet depth. Here sunlight no longer penetrates, and plants must have this to grow. Also the coral polyp feeds on floating life in the sea, trapping this with stinging tentacles. A coral reef has been described as "a flower garden where all the plants are animals". Another description of such a reef is "a living flypaper", entrapping all life that floats on it. However, the coral polyp is only partly responsible for the growth of the reef. Lime secreting algae

RAISED BEACH: *This limestone ledge shows where the sea once wore away a beach platform when the sea was about five feet higher than it is today*

also play their part, as well as a huge variety of other life.

Fringing Reefs

Around the coast are islands that are obviously pieces of the mainland cut off either by a rising sea or a sinking land. East and West Wallaby islands in the Abrolhos possess small marsupials; this indicates that these animals must have been there when the islands were cut off. Similarly in the Great Barrier Reef there are islands, like Hinchinbrook, which are obviously pieces of the mainland. Along the coast and the shores of these islands fringing reefs grow.

Barrier Reef

There has been much argument about how barrier reefs and coral atolls originated. Probably the theory that has most support is one first put forward by the famous naturalist Charles Darwin. Corals grow very rapidly, and if the land sank slowly the fringing coral reef would continue to grow. The outer edge of the reef would receive more food than the inner, and the reef would flourish here. Towards the shore a shallow lagoon would develop. Eventually the mainland would have a protective barrier reef or coral wall offshore. It has been suggested that it was this protective reef that saved the Queensland mainland from the effects of wave erosion, compared with the New South Wales coast, where there are few islands and many steep cliffs.

Coral Atoll

On an island where sinking continued, finally there would be no trace of the original land mass, only a central lagoon with a more or less circular coral reef.

Cays

Some islands could be built on emerged reefs by the collecting of sand on these. Coral cays are the result of storms separating off enough of the reef to allow the winds to wash debris around a reef platform till it collects on the lee. Gradually more and more sand accumulates and finally vegetation appears. Heron and Green islands are typical coral cays. To the north of Green Island are the Low Isles, and here the coral cay has evolved further. Shingle banks develop on the windward side and finally mangroves establish themselves on the coral mud. Low Isles were the site of the Great Barrier Reef expedition in the twenties and today are still occasionally visited by tourists. Here is the home of seabirds, though smaller cays like Michaelmas and Upolo are famous in this regard for their huge colonies of terns. Similarly the Abrolhos Islands have been a sanctuary for birds for many thousands of years, and much guano had accumulated before white settlement. Both here and on the islands of the Barrier Reef most of this guano has now been removed.

Landscape conservation

Landscape is as much in need of conservation as are Red Kangaroos or Mountain Ash. Natural landscapes are beautiful in themselves; landscapes created by man can often be so. When man fits his handiwork into a natural landscape great care is needed in order to avoid loss of beauty. For instance, a chairlift up the side of Ayers Rock would destroy the magic of this sight, and would be an act of vandalism of the worst kind. A carelessly placed road can destroy much of the charm of a natural landscape.

With the complexity of modern cities and their industries there is great need in Australia for men and women skilled in this newest of fields—landscape architecture. However, without a body of public opinion, sensitive to the beauty of our landscape, and determined to preserve it, gradually this beauty we now possess will be eroded away by apathy and greed. Careless over-grazing and negligent beach mining can perhaps be checked best at Government level; but all of us who care enough should do what we can to conserve the landscape of this land.

New South Wales

1 Australian Alps
2 Bendemeer
3 Blue Mountains
4 Botany Bay
5 Broken Bay
6 Broken Hill
7 Byron Bay
8 Darling River
9 Dubbo
10 Fitzroy Falls
11 Goulburn, and Bungonia Creek
12 Mount Kosciusko
13 New England Tableland
14 Snowy River
15 Sydney
16 Warrumbungle Range
17 Yass

Victoria

1 Bogong High Plains
2 Grampians
3 London Bridge
4 Melbourne
5 Mount Bogong
6 Port Campbell
7 Port Phillip Bay
8 Tower Hill
9 Wilson Promontory
10 Yarra River

Queensland

1 Atherton Plateau
2 Brisbane
3 Cairns
4 Cape York
5 Cloncurry
6 Cooktown
7 Gilbert River
8 Glasshouse Mountains
9 Great Barrier Reef
10 Green Island
11 Heron Island
12 Hinchinbrook Island
13 Lady Elliot Island
14 Low Isles
15 Michaelmas Cay
16 Millstream Falls
17 Molle Group
18 Mount Bartle Frere

19 Mount Beerwah
20 Mount Isa
21 Mount Lindesay
22 Normanton
23 Rockhampton
24 Torres Strait

South Australia

1 Adelaide
2 Anxious Bay
3 Aroona Dam
4 Blue Lake, and Mount Gambier
5 Brachina Gorge
6 Cooper Creek
7 Great Sandy Desert
8 Iron Knob
9 Kanyaka
10 Koonalda
11 Lake Albert
12 Lake Alexandrina
13 Lake Callabonna
14 Lake Eyre
15 Lake Frome
16 Lake Gregory
17 Mount Lofty
18 Murray River
19 Nullarbor Plain
20 Wilpena Pound

Western Australia

1 Abrolhos
2 Archipelago of the Recherche
3 Augusta
4 Broome
5 Canning Stock Route
6 Carnarvon
7 Dales Gorge
8 Darling Scarp
9 Derby
10 Esperance
11 Eucla
12 Geikie Gorge
13 Goddard's Creek
14 Hall's Creek
15 Hamelin Pool
16 Hamersley Range
17 Kalgoorlie
18 Kimberly Division
19 King Leopold Range
20 Lake Cowan
21 Lake Disappointment

22 Mount Bruce
23 Mount Ragged
24 Napier Range
25 Northam
26 Perth
27 Pilbara Division
28 Porongorups
29 Queen Victoria Spring
30 Rottnest Island
31 Shark Bay
32 Stirling Range
33 Tunnel Creek
34 Wave Rock, and Hyden
35 Wiluna
36 Winjana Gorge
37 Wittenoom
38 Wolf Creek Crater

Northern Territory

1 Alice Springs
2 Ayers Rock
3 Arnhem Land
4 Barkly Tableland
5 Boxhole
6 Chambers Pillar
7 Darwin
8 Devil's Marbles
9 Finke River
10 Glen Helen Gorge
11 Henbury
12 Katherine Gorge
13 Krichauff Range
14 Macdonnell Ranges
15 Mount Conner
16 Mount Olga
17 Musgrave Ranges
18 Standley Chasm
19 Tennant Creek
20 Yuendumu

Tasmania

1 Ben Lomond
2 Cradle Mountain
3 Eaglehawk Neck
4 Hobart
5 King River Gorge
6 Lake St Clair
7 Mount Barrow
8 Port Davey
9 Russell Falls
10 Tasman Peninsula

LOCATIONS

128

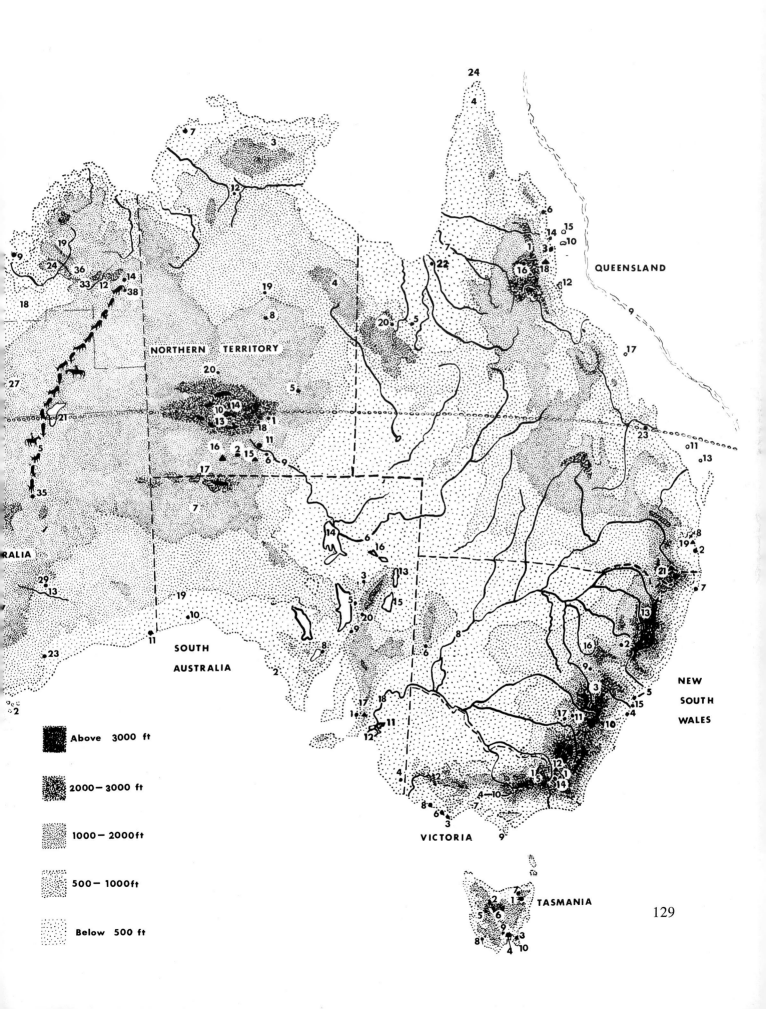

QUEENSLAND

NORTHERN TERRITORY

SOUTH
AUSTRALIA

NEW
SOUTH
WALES

VICTORIA

TASMANIA

Above 3000 ft

2000 — 3000 ft

1000 — 2000ft

500 — 1000ft

Below 500 ft

129

Index

Front cover

Wave Rock, shown on the front of the jacket of this book, has become one of the tourist attractions of Western Australia. Quite how this wave formed in the gneissic granite of the rock is a puzzle. Many similar waves are found in the rock outcrops of the wheatbelt, though this, the Hyden Wave Rock, is the most spectacular. On a smaller scale a somewhat similar wave occurs on Ayers Rock.

Photographs

All photographs in this book are by the author except Fitzroy Falls, Lake Cave, Wolf Creek meteorite crater, Aroona Dam country, the King Leopolds, Chambers Pillar, freshwater lake, Katherine Gorge, stalactites (Augusta, Western Australia), cave (Margaret River, Western Australia), Grampians, Mount Bogong, Mount Wellington, Port Davey, Crater Lake, Cradle Mountain, Barn Bluff, fretted rock, from the AUSTRALIAN NEWS AND INFORMATION BUREAU; Anxious Bay, Recherche Archipelago, Cooper Creek, Krichauff Range, Ayers Rock, Cooper Creek entering Lake Eyre, sand dune country north of the Finke River, Lake Eyre, Murray River, Lake St Clair, tessellated pavements, from the AUSTRALIAN NATIONAL TRAVEL ASSOCIATION; aerial scene in the Australian Alps, the Darling River, Barrenjoey, from the LANDS DEPARTMENT OF NEW SOUTH WALES; limestone valley, from BRUCE SEMLER; Geikie Gorge, from N. BEECK; Lion Island, Warrumbungle Range, from IAN MACARTHUR; coral reef and red sand dune, from ERIC WORRELL.

Reading List

This reading list is not intended to be exhaustive, and new books are coming out every year. For a general discussion on new ideas in geomorphology I can recommend G. K. Drury, *The Face of the Earth*, Pelican.

AUSTRALIA IN GENERAL
The Australian Encyclopaedia
C. F. Laseron, *The Face of Australia*. Angus and Robertson.
C.S.I.R.O., *The Australian Environment*. Melbourne University Press.
E. C. F. Bird, *Coastal Landforms*. Australian National University.
E. Clarke, R. T. Prider, and C. Teichert, *Elements of Geology*. W.A. University Press.

STATE BOOKS
State Year Books. In addition there are large numbers of regional works.
E. Sherborn Mills, *The Physiography of Victoria*. Whitcombe and Tombs Pty Ltd.
J. T. Jutson, *The Physiography of Western Australia*. Government Printer.
Geological Society of Australia. This society has produced a series of books dealing with the geology of each State.
G. J. Fish and M. L. Yaxley, Teaching Aids Publication 62, Education Department, Tasmania.

LADY ELLIOTT ISLAND: *Only a line of Pisonia trees withstands the ravages of goats which have reduced this island to a rocky desert (Queensland)*